GREAT INVENTIONS

GREAT INVENTIONS

100 INVENTIONS THAT HAVE SHAPED OUR WORLD

Susie Behar and Robert Yarham

igloo

Published in 2007
by Igloo Books Ltd
Cottage Farm
Sywell
NN6 0BJ
www.igloo-books.com

10 9 8 7 6 5 4 3 2 1

ISBN: 978-1-84561-935-0

Designed by
the bridgewater book company

Printed in China

Contents

Introduction 6

The Airplane 8
The Sundial 10
Glasses 12
The Battery 13
Electricity 14
The Laser 16
Velcro® 18
The Stirrup 19
The Oil Rig 20
The Escalator 22
The Calendar 23
The Wheel 24
The Lighthouse 26
Soap 28
The Mini Skirt 29
The Car 30
Writing 32
The Polygraph 34
Nylon 35
Gunpowder and Fireworks 36
The Telephone 38
Antibiotics 40
The Plow 41
The Sewing Machine 42
The Helicopter 44
The Nuclear Reactor 46
Contact Lenses 47
The Computer 48
The Suspension Bridge 50
Acupuncture 52
The Paper Clip 53
The Satellite 54
The Cotton Gin 56

The Stiletto Heel 57
The Playing Card 58
The Jet Engine 60
Compact Discs 62
The Printing Press 64
The Catseye Road Reflector 65
The Electric Motor 66
The Parachute 68
The Abacus 70
Jeans 71
X-Rays 72
Paper 74
The Camera 76
The Ski Lift 78
Braille 79
The Ejector Seat 80
The Telescope 82
The ATM 84
The Bow and Arrow 85
The Hologram 86
The Aspirin 87
The Chronometer 88
The Cell Phone 90
The Airbag 92
The Newspaper 94
The Lava® Lamp 95
The Motion Picture 96
The Windmill 98
The Diving Suit 100
Anesthetic 101
The Clock 102
The Skyscraper 104
Fire 106
The Cocktail Umbrella 108
The Lock and Key 109

The Calculator 110
Roller Skates 112
Dynamite 114
The Magnetic Compass 116
The Bikini 117
Solar Power 118
Plastic Surgery 120
The Roller Coaster 122
The Bicycle 124
The Hammock 126
The Typewriter 127
The Global Positioning System 128
The Radio 130
The Tea Bag 132
The Fire Extinguisher 133
Chess 134
The Steam Engine 136
The Zipper 138
Vaccination 139
The World Wide Web 140
Plumbing 142
The Refrigerator 144
The Yo-yo 145
The Neon Light 146
Bungee Jump 148
The Production Line 150
The Fountain Pen 152
The Supermarket 153
The Hovercraft 154
The Television 156
Chocolate 158

Picture Credits 160

INTRODUCTION

From the zipper to the light bulb, no invention arrives out of "thin air" and, for many of the inventions in this book, there is no one clear inventor because every small development takes place on the back of a previous one. What is remarkable is how "great minds" do seem to "think alike". While Thomas Edison was working on his theory and application of DC electricity, Nicholas Tesla was experimenting with AC electricity. Both Alexander Graham Bell and Antonio Meucci were working on the development of the telephone at the same time and the two men now vie in the history books for credit for this great invention.

Since the beginning of time, humankind has tried to harness and control the the power of nature. It has attempted and succeeded in its various endeavors in measuring time, making fire, using the power of steam, and—in the case of vaccination—even using viruses to fight viruses. Many of the inventions in this book were considered and written about by the ancient civilizations of Rome, Greece, China, and Persia. While it may be obvious that the development of the wheel and the plow began with the earliest civilizations, it is surprising to learn that so to did the forerunners of modern paper, aspirin, plastic surgery, and the steam engine.

Why do people invent?
Is necessity indeed the mother of invention? Time and time again, we see that inventors respond to a pressing need—such as the need for fire to keep warm and cook or the need for transport—and somehow, someone, somewhere, produces an answer. For example, the appalling sanitary conditions in industrialized countries in the mid-19th century meant that new sewers and a system of disposing of waste was necessary to stop the spread of disease—it is at this time that the flush toilet came into its own. But it isn't only necessity that is responsible for new inventions. The enquiring mind and the desire for things to be bigger, better, and faster, and for life to be more comfortable, all play a part in innovation.

Certain names crop up again and again in any book of great inventions, and this book is no exception. Leonardo da Vinci had numerous ideas that he sketched in his notebooks, which centuries later became reality: the helicopter, roller skates, contact lenses, the parachute, the diving suit, and the bicycle to name but a few. Thomas Edison is another frequently appearing name when it comes to inventions. He is

responsible for electric power, the lightbulb, and the phonograph, and he improved the telephone, and much more. Sir Humphry Davy, inventor of the miners' lamp, was also responsible for discovering laughing gas.

Gritty determination and a bit of luck

Some of the greatest and most useful inventions were accidental and discovered as a by-product of something else. The tea bag was developed by a tea merchant who wanted an easy way of sending samples to customers and so put small amounts of tea in silk bags. The X-ray was discovered by a scientist experimenting with the newly developed Crookes tube, and the zipper was originally intended for fastening boots.

Is there any one quality that defines an inventor? If there is, it is perhaps gritty determination. Many of these great inventions took years to perfect. It took Guglielmo Marconi over 20 years to fully develop his ideas for radio communication. And some ideas had to wait for the necessary technology to catch up with them. For example, though the initial idea for the hologram was in existence in the 1940s, it wasn't until the invention of the laser beam in the 1960s that the science of holography could finally be developed.

The inventions in this book range from life-saving innovations, such as antibiotics and vaccinations, to the frivolous ones, such as the mini skirt and the yo-yo. Each has a unique and fascinating history, and each depends on the brilliantly creative minds of the inventors. All of the inventions in this book have transformed, effected, or influenced humankind and culture. Sometimes, the true consequence of an invention can only be known years after its arrival; the car and the nuclear reactor fit into this category.

Is there a greatest great invention? Fire? The wheel? The computer or the internet? It is impossible to say. Civilization as we now know it is the result of the numerous inventions that Man has developed since the beginning of existence. But humankind is never satisfied. From the telephone to the cell phone, from the abacus to the calculator to the computer, from the glider to the jet engine, Man's inventiveness knows no barriers—except, perhaps, the physically impossible, and even that can change in time. Who knows what the inventors of the 21st century will create?

THE AIRPLANE

INVENTORS Orville Wright and Wilbur Wright   **DATE** 1903   **COUNTRY** USA

The inventors of the airplane were two brothers, Wilbur and Orville Wright, who were printers and bicycle builders from Ohio. Having taught themselves engineering, they began to experiment with home-built flying machines. By 1900 they had produced a glider and, by 1903, a powered aircraft.

ABOVE The Wrights' powered Flyer III flew 20 miles (32 kilometers) in 33 minutes in 1905, the 46th flight of a Wright airplane.

RIGHT The Wright stuff: the two brothers Orville (left) and Wilbur Wright. They made a promise to their father never to fly together in case of accidents.

On its maiden flight, this very first airplane—patented as a flying machine and named the Kitty Hawk—soared to an altitude of 10 feet (3 meters) and traveled 120 feet (40 meters). It landed a mere 12 seconds after take-off. It was this shaky start that ushered in the age of aviation, and in 1905 the brothers built a machine that stayed in the air for an extended period of time.

The Wright brothers' airplane was ultimately to transform the way that people traveled, traded, and waged war. In the 1930s new developments led to the invention of the jet engine. The first jet aircraft was designed by a German, Hans von Ohain. It flew in 1939, albeit imperfectly. It would take another five years for German scientists to perfect the design.

THE ONLY MODE OF TRANSPORT FASTER THAN THE AIRPLANE IS THE ROCKET. SUPERSONIC AIRCRAFT CAN ACTUALLY REACH SPEEDS MANY TIMES FASTER THAN THE SPEED OF SOUND.

SUNDIAL

INVENTOR Unknown **DATE** Ancient **COUNTRY** Unknown

The lives of ancient people were dominated by the sun and the seasons—Stonehenge in England (built about 3200 BCE) is believed to have been erected as a temple to the sun and possibly as a calendar to chart the seasons.

Timekeeping almost certainly began by pushing a stick into the ground and noting the changing position of its shadow. Similarly, the ancient Egyptians must have noted this effect from the obelisks they were building, and they built sundials as well as other devices for monitoring the positions of stars. Sundials are mentioned in the Bible, in ancient Babylonian writings, and in documents from ancient China.

RIGHT A woodcut from 1508 showing the Greek astronomer Ptolemy observing the moon and stars with a quadrant.

One problem with these early, simple "clocks" is that the divisions would have been longer in the summer than in the winter as the length of the days increased. The concept of hours being constant throughout the summer and winter would be a long time coming.

Ptolemy, the Greek astronomer and mathematician living in the 2nd century CE, did much work on the sundial, and invoked complicated mathematics to improve the designs. In short, it was proven that if a shadow from a slanting object parallel to the axis of the earth is used, it can give an accurate division of the day regardless of the time of the year.

From the 15th to the 18th centuries sundials came into use in Europe, including those giving equal hours. When mechanical clocks were invented in the 14th century, and continuing until the 18th century, sundials were used to check their accuracy. Developments in the accuracy and mass-production of mechanical clocks (see page 102) meant that sundials quickly fell into disuse; unlike sundials, they could be used at night and when it was cloudy.

THE ANCIENT ROMANS ALSO USED SUNDIALS,
EVEN MAKING POCKET VERSIONS, PERHAPS
THE FORERUNNERS OF TODAY'S WRISTWATCHES.

GLASSES

INVENTOR Abbas Ibn Firnas   **DATE** 9th century   **COUNTRY** Spain

ABOVE Made from light-weight and strong materials, today's frames are more than funtional—they are often used as fashion statements.

The ancient Greeks understood the magnification properties of glass around the 4th century BC, but it was Ptolemy in about 150 CE who first wrote about diffraction, or bending, of light. It was also reported that the Roman emperor Nero used a cut emerald to watch gladiatorial games.

However, "eyeglasses"—lenses to magnify an object originally mounted in a frame to be held up to the eye—were first made in the 9th century in Spain by the Arab Abbas Ibn Firnas. They were manufactured for about 200 years in Spain, with the Chinese adopting them, possibly as a result of trade with Arabs, in the 13th century.

Eyeglasses did not resurface in Europe again, however, until around 1270 in Italy, when it is thought that glasses with lenses mounted in a frame worn on the nose—a form more familiar to us today—were invented. Although the vague date of invention is recorded, their inventor is not. The first pictorial record of glasses is in a painting of a cardinal by Tomaso da Modena, dated 1352. The invention of the printing press about 100 years later, and the subsequent increase in the literate population, ensured that there would be a surge in demand for glasses.

Glasses have been substantially improved as a result of a number of innovations—including bifocals invented by the American Benjamin Franklin in 1784, combining two lenses in one glass for distance and close viewing, and lenses to correct astigmatisms invented by British astronomer George Airey in 1827. Improvements in materials technology has also enabled frames and lenses to become much stronger and lighter. Today, contact lenses (soft lenses sitting in direct contact on the surface of the eye) and corrective laser surgery are additional forms of sight correction, but glasses are still widely used.

WEARING GLASSES HAS LONG BEEN ASSOCIATED WITH A STEREOTYPE OF INTELLIGENCE.

THE BATTERY

INVENTOR Alessandro Volta **DATE** 1800 **COUNTRY** Italy

An Italian physics professor, Alessandro Volta, invented the battery in 1800. He was trying to prove that electricity could be produced independently of living creatures and, surmised correctly, that it could be created chemically. He placed a pair of copper and zinc discs together, separated by paper soaked in salt water, and found that he could generate an electrical current.

The electrical charge was small, however, so he tried to increase it by placing many discs on top of each other—this came to be known as the "Voltaic Pile." All subsequent advances in electricity came from Volta's work.

Within a few years batteries had been invented that could be mass-produced. The French physicist Gaston Planté invented the first rechargeable battery in 1859. A leap forward to the 1950s sees the invention of the first solar battery. Solar batteries convert the sun's energy into electricity. In a world of dwindling resources, the possibility of solar-charged machines, such as cars, had led to a new interest in this 19th-century invention, and today scientists are working on producing practical solar-powered cars for consumers.

A battery works by mixing two or more metals in a certain way to make electricity. It converts chemical energy into electrical energy. The current produced in a battery is called direct current (DC) because the electrons flow in just one direction.

BELOW Alessandro Volta demonstrates his "Voltaic Pile" to Napoleon in Paris in 1801.

ELECTRICITY

DISCOVERER Thales of Miletus   **DATE** 600 BCE   **COUNTRY** Ancient Greece

Early humankind used wood and peat fires to generate light and warmth. As civilization progressed oil lamps, gas lights, and candles were used for lighting, and coal-burning stoves warmed houses. However, as early as 600 BCE in ancient Greece, Thales of Miletus had discovered that rubbing amber against a fur cloth would attract particles of straw.

RIGHT Nikola Tesla contributed many breakthroughs in the fields of electricity and magnetism, but some extraordinary claims led to him being ostracized by the scientific community.

Centuries later, in 1600, this effect was investigated by Dr. William Gilbert who first wrote of the word "electric" in a report on the theory of magnetism. Gradually the principles of electricity began to be understood, but it was with Thomas Edison's invention of the electric light bulb in 1878 (see page 121) that the era of electric power began. Along with the light bulb, Edison invented more than 2,000 new products, including switches, fuses, sockets, and meters. By September of 1882 Edison had opened a central station in Manhattan, New York, and was able to supply electricity to a square mile of New York.

Along with Edison, the other great inventor in this area was Croatian-born Nikola Tesla. In the late 1800s he pioneered the generation, transmission, and use of alternating current (AC) electricity, which can be transmitted over much greater distances than direct current (DC), which Edison had used. AC made it possible for people to have electricity in their homes. It is Tesla's AC current that we use today, allowing us all the electric conveniences of modern life.

ELECTRICITY DOESN'T MOVE THROUGH A WIRE BUT THROUGH A FIELD AROUND THE WIRE.

A BOLT OF LIGHTNING, LASTING LESS THAN A SECOND, CAN MEASURE UP TO THREE MILLION VOLTS.

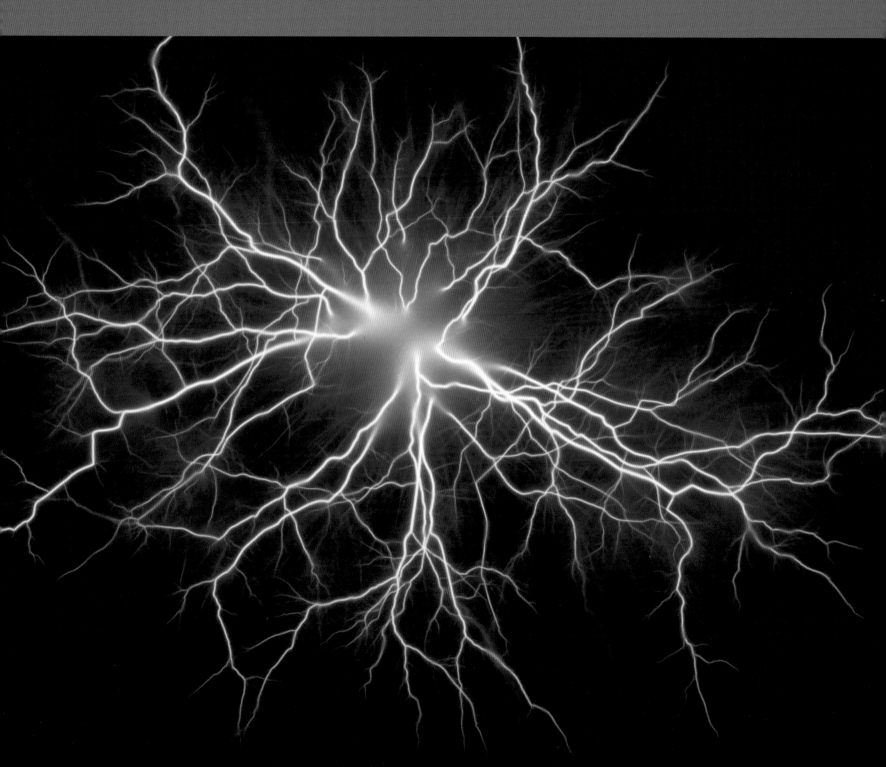

THE LASER

INVENTOR Disputed   **DATE** 1960   **COUNTRY** USA

A laser is a device that generates and focuses a high-intensity beam of light, and derives its name from an acronym describing it: Light Amplification by Stimulated Emission of Radiation.

RIGHT Theodore Maiman and a ruby crystal from which he produced the first working laser.

A laser works by exciting the atoms in a substance to the point where the light waves passing through the substance stimulate more light emission than absorption, amplifying the light particles being emitted by the atoms, and producing a concentrated narrow beam of light of a single wavelength.

Laser production came about through the efforts of Art Schawlow and Charles Townes who had been working on producing "masers" at Bell Labs in New Jersey. Masers produce lower wavelength (microwave) energy by a similar process of amplification. Schawlow and Townes published a paper in 1958 describing lasers, and a working laser was first produced by Theodore Maiman at the Hughes Research Laboratory at Malibu in California in 1960. He was awarded the patent with Schawlow that year. Maiman used a cylinder of ruby excited by a powerful flashgun and was able to produce short pulses of red light. He then used other media, such as gases, to generate a beam. Helium-neon lasers, now very widely used for low-power applications, were formulated by Ali Javan, an Iranian physicist working at Bell Labs, in 1960.

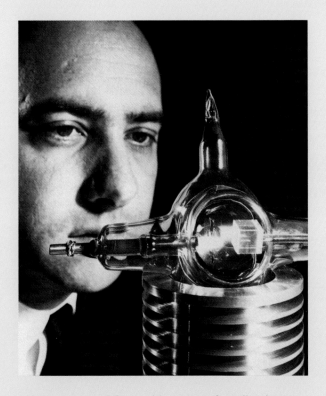

Lasers are used for a wide range of applications: to project straight lines and measure distances in surveying, for eye surgery, in compact disc (CD) and digital versatile disc (DVD) players and recorders, and in laser printers. High-powered carbon dioxide lasers are used to cut and form metal.

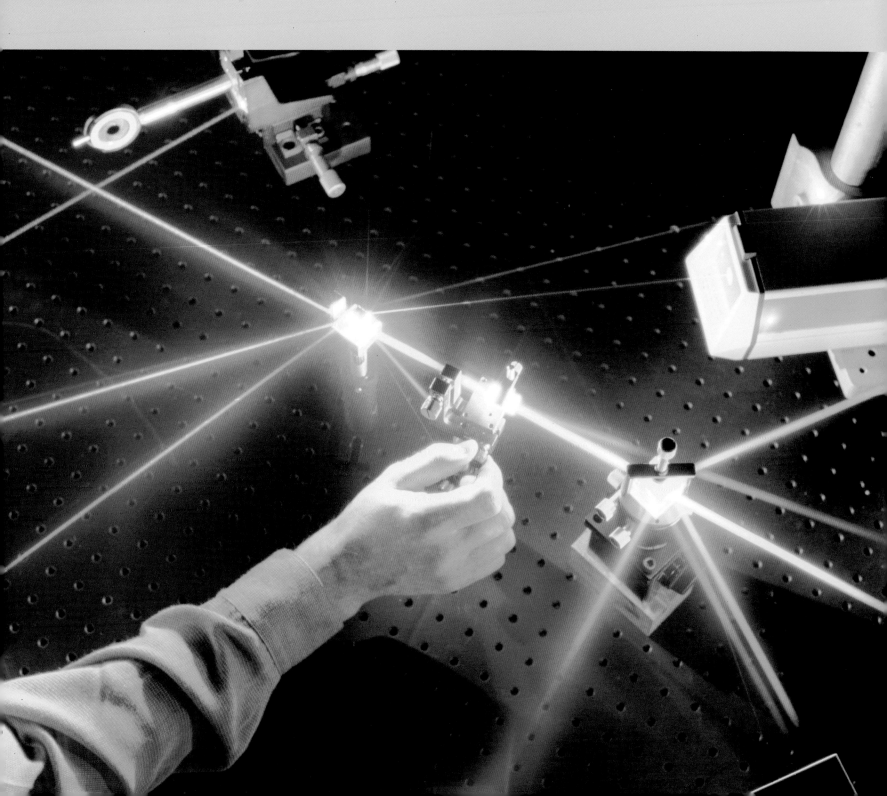

VELCRO®

INVENTOR George de Mestral   **DATE** 1948   **COUNTRY** Switzerland

Velcro® is the brandname of fabric hook-and-loop fasteners made in the USA. On a summer's day in 1948, a Swiss amateur mountaineer and engineer, George de Mestral, took his dog for a walk in the Alps.

RIGHT Strands of Velcro® consist of thousands of tiny hooks on one strip and thousands of tiny loops on the opposing strip.

Mestral and his dog returned home covered with burrs (plant seed sacs that cling to animal fur in order to be dispersed). When he examined the burrs under a microscope, Mestral saw that the small hooks on the seed sacs enabled the burrs to cling to fabric and hair.

Mestral hit upon the idea that two materials could be bound in a similar way. It took him eight years to perfect the invention. The final fastener consisted of two strips of nylon fabric. One strip contained thousands of small hooks; the other strip small loops. When the two strips were put together, they formed a strong bond. Mestral called his invention "Velcro" after the French words "velours," meaning velvet, and "crochet," meaning hook.

His design was finally patented in 1955. He formed Velcro Industries to manufacture his invention and sold over 60 million yards of Velcro® per year.

Today Velcro® is used on numerous products, from clothing to children's toys. It even helped hold a human heart together during the first artificial-heart operation.

THE STIRRUP

INVENTOR Unknown **DATE** 4th century CE **COUNTRY** China

A stirrup is a hoop connected to the saddle through which horse riders place their feet and exert control over their horses. Although humans had been riding horses and harnessing them to carts and chariots for thousands of years, the stirrup came surprisingly late in the history of riding development.

BELOW Today's stirrups are basically the same shape and fulfil the same purpose as the primitive loops used hundreds of years ago.

It is thought that early primitive forms of the stirrup were no more than loops of rope or leather into which the feet could be fitted. The first real stirrups were developed in China in the 4th century CE. They improved the stability of the rider and, from this time onward, gave cavalry much greater maneuverability and speed. The Mongol armies that swept into China and westward as far as Eastern Europe used them, bearing testimony to the formidable force the stirrup had enabled mounted cavalry to become. Stirrups had been introduced to Europe before that time, however, via earlier invaders who preceded the Mongols. The Vikings had ridden with stirrups around 1,000 CE and their use had spread throughout the rest of Europe.

There are potential dangers in using stirrups. If thrown from the horse, the rider's foot can be caught up in the stirrup and the rider to be dragged along, or injury can be caused if too much weight is put upon the wrong part of the foot. Recent design improvements have lessened these risks. Historically stirrups were iron but now the best are made from stainless steel or aluminium.

THE OIL RIG

INVENTOR Edwin L. Drake   **DATE** 1859   **COUNTRY** USA

ABOVE Drake is pictured (in a tall hat) in front of his rig in Pennsylvania talking to an engineer while the labourers stand in the background.

Oil is a fossil fuel formed by decaying plant and animal matter being pressurized under many layers of sediment built up over millions of years. From time to time, cracks in the overlying rock appear, allowing the oil to seep to the surface, creating pools of oil or "seeps."

The properties of oil found in these seeps were well known and exploited for many centuries for medicine, lighting, waterproofing, and construction. But it was in the mid-1800s when oil deposits were first extracted from deep underground.

Edwin L. Drake was employed by the Seneca Oil Company to extract crude oil, or petroleum, from seeps in Pennsylvania. He and his workmen had tried to dig down into the ground to find an oil deposit underneath one such seep, but water flooded the hole. He erected a tower, or derrick, and set up a steam engine to continuously raise and drop the drill, chipping away at the rock below. Drake solved the problems of flooding and cave-in by lowering connecting lengths of cast-iron tubing into the hole to form a drive pipe, through which the drill was threaded. On August 27, 1859, at a depth of 69 feet (21 meters), Drake struck the deposit, the hole producing 35 barrels a day.

Drake did not patent his rig, however, and, ironically, lost his money in oil speculation when his methods enabled many other oil deposits to be exploited, causing oil prices to crash. Since then, more advanced types of drilling have been developed, such as rotary drilling, where the drill bit is attached to sections of pipe and spun by an engine at the base of the derrick. The bit is continuously lubricated and cooled with a fluid known as drilling mud.

> **"THE OIL CAN IS MIGHTIER THAN THE SWORD."**
> **EVERETT DIRKSEN**

ABOVE Oil platforms are constructed at sea to house the rig, personnel, and machinery required to extract oil from the sea bed.

THE FIRST OFFSHORE OIL RIG WAS BUILT IN SUMMERLAND, CALIFORNIA, IN 1887 BY H.L. WILLIAMS, USING A WHARF EXTENDING 300 FEET (100 METERS). BUT THE FIRST BUILT OUT OF SIGHT OF LAND WAS DEVELOPED BY THE KERR-MCGEE CORPORATION IN 1947, OFF THE LOUISIANA COAST.

THE ESCALATOR

INVENTOR Charles Seeberger **DATE** 1899 **COUNTRY** USA

Moving elevator belts to carry goods to the upper levels of buildings were commonplace by the 1900s, found in factories, on agricultural machinery, and in many other industrial settings. These consisted of a motorized looped belt, sometimes with slats to prevent the transported goods from slipping.

ABOVE An 1893 illustration of an electrically powered escalator at Cortland Street Station in New York, USA.

The concept of such a device for carrying people was probably first realized in the patent for a steam-driven machine in 1859. The moving stairway type of elevator was patented in 1892 by a Jesse Reno in the USA, who used it as a fairground attraction. The escalator, as we now know it, is credited to one Charles Seeberger whose patented design was made by the Otis factory in New York in 1899. This wooden-stepped escalator won first prize at the 1900 Paris Exposition. The company's engineers continued to improve the original designs and Otis became synonymous with the word "escalator."

Since then, Otis escalators have been installed in many thousands of buildings all over the world, and the company is still producing them although it is now a subsidiary of United Technologies. The name escalator became a protected trademark of the Otis company, which bought out the Jesse Reno patents as well as those from Seeberger. The Otis company lost the exclusive right to the word in 1950, the US Patent Office ruling "escalator" to be just a term for the moving staircase.

THE CALENDAR

INVENTOR Unknown **DATE** Unknown **COUNTRY** Unknown

It would seem that from the beginning of man's history on earth, he has attempted to measure time.

Scratched lines and gouged holes in sticks and bones made by ice-age hunters in Europe over 20,000 years ago are thought to have been attempts to record the days between phases of the moon.

In warmer climates such as southern Europe, Africa, and the Middle East, the moon was used to mark time. It is also clear that since their invention, calendars have been used to fix events such as harvests or religious festivals.

Several different calendars are used throughout the world, but the most widely deployed is the Gregorian calendar. It was first proposed by a doctor, Aloysius Lilius, and was decreed by Pope Gregory XIII in 1582 via the papal bull. Years in the calendar are numbered from the traditional birth year of Jesus, which has been labeled the "Anno Domini" (AD) era, and is sometimes labeled the "Common Era" or the "Christian Era" (CE). The Gregorian calendar was devised both because an earlier calendar, the Julian calendar, was flawed. The Gregorian calendar, based on the cycles of the sun and moon, followed the real solar cycle more closely than the Julian calendar.

THE EARLIEST KNOWN DATE IS 4236 BCE, WHEN THE EGYPTIAN CALENDAR WAS FOUNDED.

RIGHT The Gregorian calendar used today is named for Pope Gregory XIII who instituted its adoption by papal bull in 1582.

THE WHEEL

INVENTOR Unknown **DATE** 3500 BCE **COUNTRY** Mesopotamia

The invention of the wheel is not just about transportation: its emergence was essential for the development of modern technology. Without it there would have been no spinning wheel or water wheel, no watch gears or pulleys, no computer discs or computer mice.

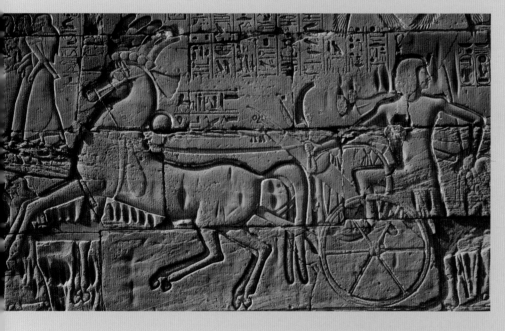

ABOVE An Egyptian relief from around 1300 BCE shows a chariot with spoked wheels being ridden into battle.

Before the invention of the wheel, objects were transported by logs. There is evidence that this method was used in the Paleolithic era (15,000 to 750,000 years ago). Later fixed platforms (sledges) were added to the log rollers to make transportation easier. The most important development leading the invention of the wheel was the axle. The wood between the grooves that the sledge made on the rollers was cut away to create an axle.

The earliest known use of the wheel was as a potter's wheel in Mesopotamia (part of modern-day Iraq) in 3500 BCE. The first use of the wheel for transportation was probably on Mesopotamian chariots in 3200 BCE. Subsequent improvements were made by the Egyptians, who developed wheels with spokes to lighten the wheel. Spoked wheels have been found in chariots of around 2000 BCE. The Greeks and Romans made further refinements.

Tires were developed to protect the wheel from damage. The first wheel "covers" were made from

leather, iron, wood, and later, rubber. The pneumatic tire was first patented in 1845 by R.W. Thompson for use on bicycles. Thompson's invention of an air-filled tire was later further refined by a Scottish veterinarian John Dunlop in 1888. Dunlop's idea came out of his desire to help prevent the headaches his young son suffered when riding his tricycle.

LEFT John Dunlop, who invented the first practical pneumatic tyre for his son's tricycle. He patented the idea in 1888 and founded Dunlop Tyres.

THE LIGHTHOUSE

INVENTOR Ancient Egyptians   **DATE** 250 BC   **COUNTRY** Egypt

Since ancient times, lights have been used to guide sailors into harbors, or to warn them of dangerous waters and rocks. These early lights probably consisted of fires mounted on coastal hillsides or platforms. The ancient Egyptians built the first recorded lighthouse in around 250 BCE on the island of Pharos at the mouth of the harbor of Alexandria.

RIGHT The third Eddystone Lighthouse, built by John Smeaton between 1756 and 1759 and used until 1877, has been rebuilt on Plymouth Hoe.

Designed by Sostratus for the pharaoh Ptolemy Soter, and now estimated to have stood between 350 and 400 feet tall, was one of the ancient Seven Wonders of the World. A large mirror at the tower's summit is said to have reflected the sun during the day, and a fire during the night. It stood for around 1,500 years until it was fatally damaged by a series of earthquakes in the early 1300s.

There were many other lighthouses throughout the ancient world, built by the Phoenicians, Romans, and Arabs, and examples include the Roman lighthouses at Dover in England, built in around 50 CE, and the Hercules Tower at La Coruña in Spain. The Mayans also built lighthouses to guide their sailors through dangerous reefs in the 13th century.

The first lighthouse to be built on a rock offshore was the Eddystone Lighthouse in English waters, 13 miles southwest of Plymouth, completed in 1698. This was also the first lighthouse to

enclose lighted candles in a glass lantern, protecting the light and projecting it a greater distance.

Lighthouse technology took a leap forward in 1822 with the invention by a Frenchman, Augustin Fresnel, of a large lens to substantially magnify the light and focus it into a beam. The first Fresnel lens, which consisted of many small prisms of glass, was installed in 1822 in the

Cardovan Tower lighthouse on the Gironde river in southwest France. It could be seen more than 20 miles (32 kilometers) away.

Although modern GPS and sonar enable sailors to navigate through dangerous stretches of water, lighthouses are still used as an important visual aid, although most are now fully automated and remotely controlled.

LEFT The lower light room in the fifth Eddystone Lighthouse, built between 1878 and 1892, showing the twin burners and reflectors.

SOAP

INVENTOR Ancient Babylonians   **DATE** Unknown   **COUNTRY** Babylonia

ABOVE Advertisement for Sunlight soap in around 1890, promoting its qualities to British housewives.

Since prehistoric times people used water for cleansing themselves and their clothes. Legend has it that the first soap was produced accidentally on Mount Sapo, a site of animal sacrifice for the Ancient Romans. As the goat meat burned, fat dripped down, bonding to lye that leached out of the ashes.

The combined fat and lye flowed down the mountainside and collected in the clay of the riverbanks, where women used the clay to scrub their laundry clean. However, since no Mount Sapo is known, the story is most likely pure fiction.

In fact, evidence points to the Babylonians as the inventors of soap, since a soap-like substance has been found in ancient Babylonian containers. Egyptians and Romans used oils for bathing and soap was not widely known in Europe until the Arab invasion of the Byzantine Empire in (629 CE). Arabs had used soap since the 7th century CE, and once the invention had spread to the Mediterranean, olive oil was used instead of animal fat. In northern Europe it was the Celts who first started using soap.

THE ENGLISH SOAP-MAKING COMPANY, LEVER BROTHERS, FIRST COINED THE TERM B.O. FOR "BAD ODOR" AS PART OF THEIR MARKETING CAMPAIGN FOR THE SOAP.

MINI SKIRT

INVENTOR Disputed   **DATE** 1960s   **COUNTRY** Disputed

It was, of course, in the "swinging 60s" that the mini skirt—a very short skirt with a hemline that sits across the top of the thighs—first saw the light of day.

The bases of skirts—or hemlines—began rising markedly after World War I so that, by the 1920s, skirts were sometimes being worn above the knee. Hemlines dropped during and after World War II, however, so that, by the 1950s, younger women usually dressed in what had almost become a uniform of sweater and straight skirts worn below the knee. The time was ripe in Britain, though, for youthful rebellion against the drab conservatism that had been imposed by rationing.

The mini skirt is always associated with the name of the London fashion designer Mary Quant who, if she did not actually invent it, certainly made it popular worldwide. There is still dispute over who did invent the mini skirt, with the British designer John Bates, American designer Helen Rose, and French designer André Corrèges also being credited.

Mary Quant's early versions of the skirt in 1965 were modest affairs compared with what was to come, being just above knee level. Mini skirts became shorter and shorter, often encroaching on what might be called the decency level. Despite the ever-changing nature of fashion, the mini skirt has been embraced by each new generation.

LEFT Mini skirt from around 1970.

CO-INCIDENT WITH THE INTRODUCTION OF THE NEW FASHION IN VERY SHORT SKIRTS CAME A REVOLUTION IN LEG-WEAR— TIGHTS, OR PANTYHOSE.

ABOVE Henry Ford founded the Ford Motor Company in 1903 and quickly revolutionized manufacturing as well as the motor industry.

Possibly one of the most useful and yet also the most problematic of modern inventions, the creation of the car occurred over a period of years. The first self-propelled car was built by Nicolas Cugnot in 1769. Powered by a steam engine, it could attain speeds of up to 4 miles (6 kilometers) per hour. In 1771 Cugnot suffered the world's first car accident when he drove another speedier, steam-driven vehicle into a wall.

In 1807 François Isaac de Rivaz designed the first internal combustion engine, which used a mixture of hydrogen and oxygen to generate energy. He later developed the world's first vehicle driven by an internal combustion engine. In 1862 Jean-Joseph Etienne Lenoir built an experimental vehicle driven by a gas-engine (which he had previously invented). This could reach a speed of 2 miles (3 kilometers) per hour. These cars became popular and by 1865 could be frequently seen on the roads.

However, it was the American manufacturer Henry Ford who became the first person to mass-produce cars. Henry Ford founded the Ford Motor Company and gave America its first affordable car, the Model T, in 1908. Ford proclaimed, "I will build a car for the great multitude"—and he did. In the Model T's 19 years of production, nearly 15,500,000 were sold in the United States alone.

Ford's Model T profoundly changed America. It promoted the growth of suburbia, the creation of a national highway system, and a population more mobile than had ever before been imagined.

LEFT Introduced on 1 October 1908, the Ford Model T was easy to drive, as well as practical and cheap to own.

"THE HORSELESS CARRIAGE IS THE COMING WONDER. IT IS ONLY
A QUESTION OF A SHORT TIME WHEN THE CARRIAGES AND TRUCKS
IN EVERY LARGE CITY WILL BE RUN WITH MOTORS."
THOMAS EDISON, 1895

WRITING

INVENTORS Sumerians **DATE** 3500 BCE **COUNTRY** Mesopotamia

It cannot really be said that writing was invented, but rather it developed from the very first attempts by humankind to record things through making marks on cave walls and etchings into sand. It emerged in many different cultures and in numerous locations throughout the ancient world.

RIGHT This ancient tablet shows an example of one of the earliest written languages invented around 3,000 years BC by the Sumerians in what is now southern Iraq.

However, the Sumerians of ancient Mesopotamia are credited with inventing the earliest form of writing, which appeared around 3500 BCE on clay tablets.

The writings on these tablets are simple pictures, or pictograms, that represent an object or an idea. Clay is a difficult material on which to draw lines and curves, so the Mesopotamians eventually reduced pictograms into a series of wedge-shaped signs that were pressed into the clay with a reed stylus. This wedge-shaped writing is called "cuneiform." It was first used as a method of accounting for commercial transactions.

The Phoenicians were the first society to create an alphabet. In an alphabet symbols represent sounds, rather than pictures or ideas. In about 500 BCE the Greeks modified the Phoenician alphabet—the result still resembles the alphabet we use today. It was the Greek alphabet that first introduced vowel signs.

The "invention" of writing meant that information and record keeping was no longer dependent on memory and oral communication. It meant that ideas and news could be spread far and wide— it was the beginning of the information highway.

THE ANCIENT EGYPTIANS USED A COMPLICATED SYSTEM
OF SYMBOLS KNOWN AS HIEROGLYPHS. DIFFICULT TO LEARN,
HIEROGLYPHS PRESERVED POWER IN THE HANDS OF THE
SCRIBES WHO USED AND INTERPRETED IT.

THE POLYGRAPH

INVENTOR James Mackenzie   **DATE** 1902   **COUNTRY** USA

It has long been supposed that people undergo a number of physiological reactions caused by the stress of lying. It was not until the early 1900s that a young Harvard psychology student called William Marston first proposed measuring these reactions scientifically.

LEFT A lie detector measures the body's responses to a carefully chosen list of questions.

James Mackenzie in Scotland had invented the first "polygraph" in 1902—a device that measured a patient's pulse, blood pressure, or respiration, and recorded the results by drawing ink traces onto paper. Marston suggested that, by interrogating subjects in a certain way and recording their reactions, it would be possible to determine whether they were telling the truth.

In 1921, John Larson, a medical student at the University of California, invented the precursor to the modern polygraph, using a drum to simultaneously record a subject's involuntary physiological reactions. Leonarde Keeler developed the polygraph machine in subsequent years, adding a reading for skin conductance in 1939, and producing more compact versions for sale. Refinements of the polygraph have been developed ever since, but they still follow the same principles. More recently, a new lie detector has been invented that detects changes in temperature around a subject's eye sockets—purportedly a more accurate method of detecting whether someone is telling the truth.

The lie detector was first used in police investigations in the USA in 1924, but the results are rarely admissible as evidence in law. In fact, the use of the polygraph to determine whether a subject is telling the truth or not is still mired in controversy.

THE POLYGRAPH CAN NOT ACTUALLY DETECT LIES, AS ITS NICKNAME SUGGESTS—IT CAN ONLY DETECT WHETHER DECEPTIVE BEHAVIOR IS BEING DISPLAYED.

NYLON

INVENTOR Wallace Carothers · **DATE** 1935 · **COUNTRY** USA

Wallace Carothers was 32 years old when he was appointed director of DuPont Corporation's research center in 1928. Before this, he had studied and taught chemistry, specializing in polymers—molecules composed of long chains of repeating units of atoms.

After much experimentation, Carothers was able to develop a synthetic fiber from them. He called it nylon. DuPont described its new fiber as being "as strong as steel, as fine as a spider's web." Patented in 1935, products made from nylon began to be mass produced in 1939. Nylon stockings in particular were an immediate success. They were cheaper, easier to wash, and more durable than their silk counterparts. In its first year, DuPont sold 64 million pairs of stockings. In 1942, nylon was used to make parachutes and tents for World War II. Carothers' invention was later used in a wide variety of products, including toothbrushes, fishing lines, and surgical thread. Nylon was the forerunner of many of today's synthetic fabrics and remains the second most used synthetic fiber in the USA.

LEFT Stockings were among the most popular products made using the new synthetic fiber from 1939 onwards.

THE FIRST PRODUCT DU PONT MADE AND SOLD WITH POLYMERS WAS A TOOTHBRUSH WITH NYLON BRISTLES. THE BRUSH DRIED OUT BETWEEN USES, UNLIKE THE TRADITIONAL BOAR HAIR BRUSHES.

GUNPOWDER AND

INVENTOR Unknown   **DATE** Unknown   **COUNTRY** China

ABOVE An illustration from 1715 showing gunpowder being used in cannons, mortars, and rockets.

RIGHT Guy Fawkes was arrested under the Houses of Parliament on November 5 1605.

Gunpowder is a mixture of 70 percent potassium nitrate, 15 percent sulfur, and 15 percent charcoal, and it is used in various quantities to create explosions. A firework is a tube filled with gunpowder and other combustible material—or objects such as streamers—for decorative and display effects.

It is certain that both gunpowder and fireworks originated in China. The only doubts are when, where, and by whom they were invented. Gunpowder was invented, or more correctly discovered—perhaps accidentally—during experiments in alchemy sometime between the early 7th and early 10th centuries. Before then potassium nitrate, the component that feeds oxygen to the explosion, was known and used to make fires burn very brightly. The earliest recorded mention of fireworks as we would know them comes later, from the 12th century, a time when rockets were also being used in warfare.

From China the technology of pyrotechnics spread to Arabia where, in the 13th and 14th centuries, there are many references to the uses of gunpowder and the invention of weaponry using it. Rockets and incendiary devices were apparently used against the crusaders. This knowledge reached Europe in the 15th century and the first use of fireworks for celebratory purposes outside China is recorded in Florence.

The first recorded firework display in Britain was at the wedding of King Henry VII in 1486. They were also used in celebration of Queen Elizabeth I at Kenilworth Castle in 1570. Perhaps the best-known use of gunpowder in Britain was the alleged plot to blow up the Houses of Parliament in 1605 by Guy Fawkes and his Catholic colleagues, which gave rise to the custom of fireworks and effigy burning still practiced today.

FIREWORKS

THE TELEPHONE

INVENTOR: Disputed   **DATE** 1800s   **COUNTRY** USA

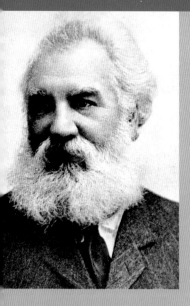

ABOVE Alexander Graham Bell patented the telephone in 1876, ushering in a revolution in communication.

RIGHT A sketch of Bell's telephone device from 1876.

Controversy surrounds the invention of the telephone. Alexander Graham Bell is usually credited as its creator, but it was actually Antonio Meucci, an Italian immigrant, who first developed the design of the "talking telegraph" in 1849.

In 1871, he filed a caveat (an intention to patent) for his design. However, personal circumstances meant Meucci was unable to renew his caveat, and in 1876 Scottish-born scientist Alexander Graham Bell, who had been working on ways to help deaf and mute people speak by recording speech vibrations, filed a patent for his version of the telephone. Amazingly, Meucci's work was overlooked until the United States House of Representatives passed a Resolution on June 11, 2002, honoring his contribution to the invention of the telephone.

Could either of these men have imagined that their work would eventually lead to the invention of the cell phone in 1978? Developed by Joel Engle and Richard Frenkiel, the cell phone came from the labs of the Bell Telephone Company, which Alexander Graham Bell's father-in-law Gardiner Hubbard founded one hundred years before, in 1878. And although we may think of the cell phone as a relatively recent invention, American police cars were using primitive cell phones way back in the 1920s.

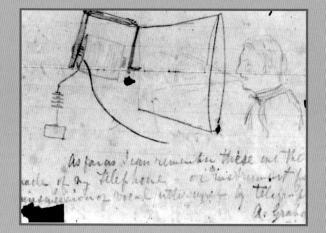

"COME HERE WATSON, I WANT YOU."

THE FIRST WORDS SPOKEN ON A TELEPHONE BY BELL TO HIS ASSISTANT, THOMAS WATSON

"THE HUMAN VOICE CARRIES ENTIRELY TOO FAR AS IT IS... AND NOW YOU FELLOWS COME ALONG AND SEEK TO COMPLICATE MATTERS."
MARK TWAIN ON THE INVENTION OF THE TELEPHONE

ANTIBIOTICS

DISCOVERER Alexander Fleming **DATE** 1928 **COUNTRY** UK

Penicillin was one of the earliest discovered antibiotics and remains one of the most widely used today. It was originally discovered by a French medical student, Ernest Duchesne, in 1896, but he could see no practical application for his discovery.

It wasn't until 1928 that penicillin was rediscovered by bacteriologist Alexander Fleming at St. Mary's Hospital in London, England. Fleming saw that a culture of staphylococcus contaminated by a blue-green mold destroyed colonies of bacteria adjacent to the mold. However, his discovery's germ-destroying qualities lasted for only a few days. Use of penicillin did not begin in earnest until the 1940s when an Australian and a German scientist, Howard Florey and Ernst Chain, developed a powdery form of the medicine.

Since the discovery of penicillin many new antibiotics have been developed, including streptomycin, which cures tuberculosis, and tetracycline, which is used to fight many bacterial infections. Antibiotics have indeed proved to be "miracle drugs" and their invention has saved millions of lives across the world.

An antibiotic is a germ-killing substance that comes from a living source, often a mold. Although it successfully combats a wide range of serious diseases, it is virtually harmless to normal tissues.

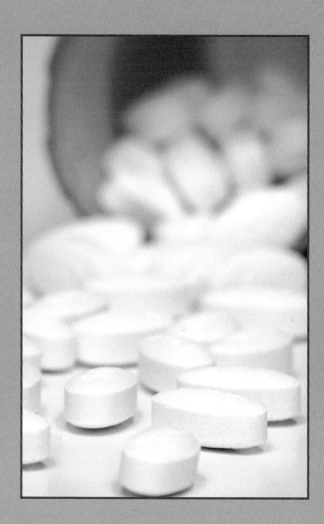

THE PLOW

INVENTOR Unknown   **DATE** around 6000 BCE   **COUNTRY** Unknown

A plow is a device for turning the soil over, to help drainage and reduce weeds, in preparation for sowing and planting crops. When our hunter-gatherer ancestors ended their nomadic life and turned to raising crops, tilling the soil must have become one of their main preoccupations.

ABOVE This ancient Egyptian wall painting shows a simple wooden plow being pulled by two oxen.

It is likely that hoeing the ground to make furrows for planting seeds was first carried out with primitive wooden implements. Development of these led to simple plows, probably drawn by oxen, it is thought, about 6000 BCE. The ancient Egyptians made a number of improvements to the plow, as seen in their wall inscriptions.

The ancient Greeks improved the plow further by fitting wheels, which made the implements easier to work with. It was probably at that time that iron was first used for the plowshares—the part that turns over the soil.

It was not until the 17th century that significant improvement to the design was made in Holland. The shape of the plowshare was changed so that the soil was more fully turned over, allowing better cultivation. In England, a Joseph Foljambe patented the Rotherham plow: it had no wheels, but an improved shape with iron covering the wearing parts. Further development was made by John Small who applied a scientific approach to the design, and the modern plow shape was born.

The advent of steam and motorized tractors from 1850 onward made plowing easier and quicker, and enabled the invention of multiple furrow plows.

THE SEWING MACHINE

INVENTOR Charles Wiesenthal   **DATE** 1755   **COUNTRY** UK

There is evidence that for over 20,000 years people have hand-sewn items. The first mechanical sewing device was invented by a German, Charles Frederick Wiesenthal, in England. He patented his double-pointed needle in 1755. The machine's practicality was limited since its design meant that the thread had to be kept short.

ABOVE Isaac Singer (seated) is shown adjusting the tension on his prototype sewing machine in 1850.

RIGHT Barthélemy Thimonnier patented the first sewing machine for practical use in 1830 in Paris.

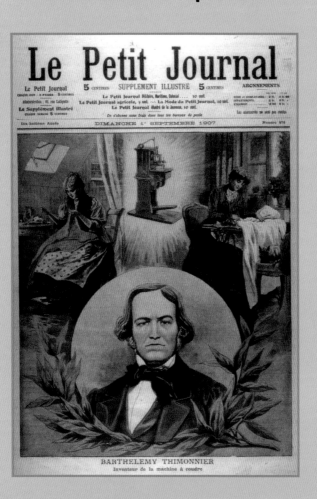

There were subsequent attempts and patents, but the real breakthrough came in 1830 when a French tailor, Barthélemy Thimonnier, invented a sewing machine made out of wood. Thimonnier's machine functioned so well that he was able to set up a garment factory that produced uniforms for the French army. However, fearing his invention would put them out of business, an angry mob of French tailors burnt it down. Thimonnier had produced the first practical sewing machine and ran the first garment factory, but he died in the poor house in 1857.

Sewing machines did not go into mass production until the 1850s, when Isaac Singer built the first commercially successful machine. The Singer machine had a needle that moved up and down rather than side to side, and was powered by a foot treadle. Earlier sewing machines had been hand-cranked.

In the 1900s the first electric machines were made. By 1926 the American patent office had

over 150,000 different models patented. Today's machines can be computer controlled, and are so advanced they can scan a pattern, duplicate it, and store it in case it is needed again.

The mechanical sewing machine helped to transform manufacturing over the course of the 19th century. Before its invention most of the manufacturing workforce operated by hand from home. By 1900 most were working in factories using powered machinery.

THE HELICOPTER

INVENTOR Igor Sikorsky   **DATE** 1939   **COUNTRY** Russia/USA

As early as the 14th century the Chinese made a toy that closely resembled a toy helicopter. It was a flying top with four rotor blades attached to a spindle. A sharp pull on the string that was wound around the spindle caused the rotors to spin upward.

ABOVE Louis Breguet's gyroplane achieved the first flight of a vertical-ascending aircraft in 1907, although he did not develop the gyroplane further until 1935.

RIGHT Igor Sikorsky's VS-300 helicopter pictured in flight in April 1941, in Connecticut, USA.

In the 16th century, the polymath Leonardo da Vinci sketched a helicopter-type flying machine in his notebooks. He wrote of his design: "If it is rotated rapidly it will fly up into the air with a corkscrewing motion."

Throughout the 19th century several inventors attempted to design working helicopters. Their main problem was that the available engine technology did not allow for an engine that was light enough to get the helicopter off the ground. With the invention of the gas turbine in the 20th century, a raft of possibilities opened up.

In 1907 the first helicopter flight, if rather short, took place. A French inventor, Louis Breguet, flew his four-rotor "Gyroplane" two feet off the ground for one minute. In 1923 a Spanish engineer, Juan de la Cierv, created the "autogyro," which proved a commercial success although it was unable to hover and could only stay in flight when moving forward—in essence the design was an airplane with large horizontal rotors.

The model for all modern single-rotor helicopters was the invention of Russian designer Igor Sikorsky. Initially Sikorsky built an amphibious aircraft, later turning his hand to helicopter design. His first helicopter, the VS-300, was flown in 1939. A later Sikorsky helicopter, the XR-4, was the first to be used by the military for purposes other than surveillance.

A HELICOPTER IS AN ASSEMBLY OF AROUND 40,000 LOOSE PIECES, FLYING MORE OR LESS IN FORMATION.

THE NUCLEAR REACTOR

DISCOVERER Enrico Fermi   **DATE** 1942   **COUNTRY** USA

ABOVE Albert Einstein was one of the scientists whose work in atomic physics led to the building of a nuclear reactor.

RIGHT A nuclear reactor core.

A nuclear reactor uses a natural process called fission, in which radioactive elements, particularly uranium 235, are unstable enough to release neutrons, which then collide with other atoms and cause a chain reaction generating heat.

Radiation was discovered by Wilhelm Roentgen in 1895, in the form of X-rays (see page 72) emitted from cathode ray tubes. His work was carried on by Henri Bequerel, who found that the salts of uranium "fogged" a covered photographic plate. Further work on radioactivity was done by Pierre and Marie Curie, the latter being mainly interested in its therapeutic uses.

In the 19th and early 20th centuries, physicists knew that the atom contained latent energy. Ernest Rutherford, the British physicist, wrote: "If it were ever possible to control at will the rate of disintegration of the radio elements, an enormous amount of energy could be obtained from a small amount of matter." Albert Einstein quantified this mathematically, producing his famous formula $E = MC^2$ (energy equals mass times a constant squared, in this case the constant being the speed of light). The first demonstration model reactor was constructed by a team led by Enrico Fermi in a Chicago athletic stadium in 1942.

The radioactive core is controlled by rods, encased in graphite, to absorb the neutrons. The rods are lowered or lifted to vary the strength of the reaction. The heat from the reaction is then used to generate steam to drive turbines that, in turn, drive electric generators. There are several varieties of reactor, including water-cooled, gas-cooled and the so-called "fast-breeder" reactors that create fissionable material.

Interestingly, in the early 20th century it was believed that radiation was good for health: there was even a radium toothpaste! The effects of radiation are now known to be deadly.

CONTACT LENSES

INVENTOR Adolf Fick   **DATE** 1887   **COUNTRY** Germany

Modern contact lenses are worn directly on the cornea of the eye. However, the very first contact lenses covered the entire eye and were so uncomfortable that they could only be worn for a few hours.

BELOW By 1999 disposable soft contact lenses were available.

In around 1508 Leonardo da Vinci sketched a primitive contact lens in one of his notebooks. Da Vinci's lens was made from a short tube that had a flat lens at one end. The tube was filled with water and held against the eye. The idea was that the water would correct the vision in the same way that curved lenses do today.

In 1887 a German doctor, Adolf Fick, made a heavy, brown glass lens that covered the eyeball and was about ¾ inches (18 millimeters) in diameter. Fick fitted the lens on animals and later on people.

In 1934 a plastic called polymethylmethacrylate was created. It was this invention that was to revolutionize contact lenses. In 1948 Californian optician Kevin Touhy created the first hard lens from the plastic; these lenses fitted onto the cornea. In 1971 the first soft lens was invented in the USA by Bausch and Lomb. Made of thin, pliable plastic, these lenses were water based and much more comfortable to wear. Later in the 1970s lenses were made of silicon, which is gas-permeable and allows oxygen through to the eye.

THE COMPUTER

INVENTOR Charles Babbage   **DATE** 1840   **COUNTRY** UK

ABOVE Charles Babbage who created a mechanical "Analytical Engine" for complex calculations, although he never completed it.

The English mathematician Charles Babbage is considered to be the inventor of the computer. In 1840, he created a sophisticated calculating machine, and called it the "Analytical Engine." It was mechanical, rather than electronic, and Babbage never completed it.

However, today's computers are based on many of the principles he used in his design. It took another 100 years before the first electronic computers were built. These were large and very heavy, such as the MARK I, which was used during World War II by the US Navy. Developed by Howard Aiken and Grace Hopper at Harvard University, it was 55 feet (16.7 meters) long and 8 feet (2.4 meters) high and filled a whole room.

Modern computers are very different, and many of the functions of everyday life are performed by computers without us even being aware of them. From turning on the television to making a telephone call, we are using a computer. Computers are found in all walks of life, ranging from running a farm to diagnosing disease, and from designing to constructing and launching a space vehicle.

"I THINK THERE IS A WORLD MARKET FOR MAYBE FIVE COMPUTERS."
THOMAS WATSON, CHAIRMAN OF IBM, 1943

LEFT An early IBM computer, designed by Howard Aiken, in Cambridge, Massachusetts in 1944.

IN 2002 THE WORLD'S SMALLEST COMPUTER WAS DEVELOPED.
AROUND A TRILLION OF THESE BIOLOGICAL COMPUTING DEVICES CAN
FIT WITHIN A DROP OF WATER. MADE OF BIOLOGICAL MOLECULES, IT IS
PROGRAMMED TO IDENTIFY CHANGES IN THE BALANCE OF MOLECULES
IN THE BODY THAT INDICATE THE PRESENCE OF CERTAIN CANCERS.

THE SUSPENSION BRIDGE

INVENTOR James Finley   **DATE** Around 1800   **COUNTRY** USA

The earliest suspension bridges were simply ropes stretched across a gorge or river, from which people could hang or crawl. Later bridges had wooden footways added between the ropes. Although people could use these primitive bridges, they were not practical for horse and carriages or heavy loads.

BELOW The suspension bridge over the Menai Straits in Wales, designed by Thomas Telford and built between 1820 to 1826.

The development of the modern suspension bridge dates from around 1800. An American inventor named James Finley filed a patent on an early version of a suspension bridge. Finley's design used towers to elevate the cables and trusses to stiffen the deck. The towers made it possible for the deck to remain perfectly flat for horses and carriages to cross; the trusses prevented the deck from swaying. This was the first rigid suspension bridge. These early suspension bridges used massive iron chain links from which the road deck was hung. The Clifton Suspension Bridge in Bristol, southwest England, designed by 24-year-old Isambard Kingdom Brunel in 1830, still has iron chain links.

It wasn't until the invention of steel wire from about 1870 that the modern suspension bridge was born. Steel, being stronger than iron but lighter, could take the weight of much longer bridges. The Brooklyn Bridge in New York was 50 percent longer than any bridge that preceded it and was the longest suspension bridge in the world at the time of its completion in 1883. Still in operation, it carries 150,000 vehicles and 3,000 pedestrians in and out of Manhattan daily. Designed by German immigrant John Roebling, it is 3,460 feet (1,055 meters) long, and is, he claimed, "the perfect equilibrium of nature."

ACUPUNCTURE

INVENTOR Unknown   **DATE** Unknown   **COUNTRY** Unknown

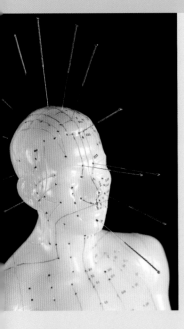

ABOVE Acupuncture is known to help in the treatment of several medical conditions by encouraging the body's production of endorphins.

RIGHT A Chinese acupuncture chart dating from the Ming Dynasty (1340s).

Acupuncture is a system of healing involving the careful insertion of very fine sterile needles into specific parts of the body.

According to traditional Chinese philosophy, good health depends on "Qi," the body's lifeforce energy, which moves in pathways across the surface of the body and deep inside the organs. Acupuncture is said to help the Qi flow in a smooth and balanced way. What is known is that the technique stimulates the body's production of endorphins, or natural painkillers, and can be effective in the treatment of a range of medical conditions.

The origins of acupuncture are uncertain but the first known medical text to feature acupuncture is *Huang Di Nei Jing* (the "Yellow Emperor's Classic of Internal Medicine"), which dates back to around 300 BCE. In 1991, a 5,000-year-old mummified body was discovered in the Alps. The body has over 50 tattoos, some of which are located on known acupuncture points, and this has led some scientists to believe that a medical system similar to acupuncture may have been practiced in central Europe during the early Bronze Age.

The first book on acupuncture written in English was *A Treatise on Acupuncturation* by James M. Churchill in 1821, but the Western medical profession only began to take an interest in the practice in the early 20th century. Today acupuncture is increasingly being used alongside conventional medicine. It provides a powerful complementary therapy, without the side-effects of conventional pharmaceutical drugs.

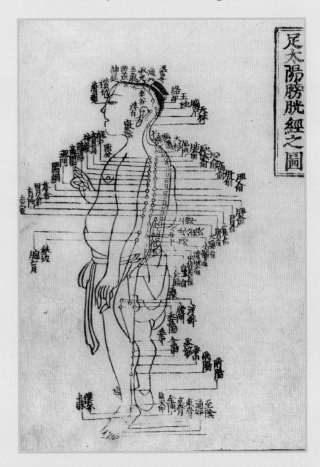

THE PAPER CLIP

INVENTOR Samuel B. Fay **DATE** 1867 **COUNTRY** USA

A paper clip is an ingenious but simple device, consisting of a thin wire wound into a flat loop, designed to hold several pieces of paper together without puncturing them.

The first design for a clip was patented by Samuel B. Fay in the USA in 1867. Originally designed to hold garments and textiles together, it was soon being sold as a device to hold two or more pieces of paper together. Ten years later, Erlman J. Wright and Joseph E. Manthei patented a refinement of the clip, designed specifically to fasten paper. This design was subsequently honed still further with additional patents.

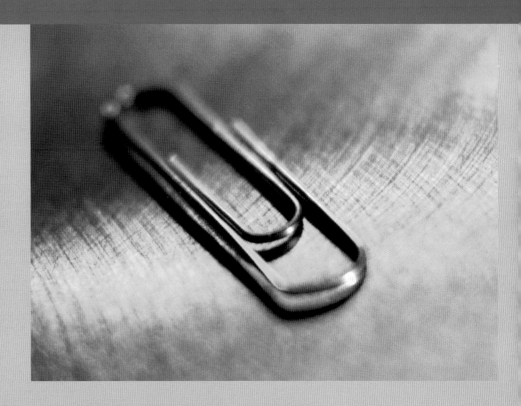

THE WORLD'S LARGEST PAPER CLIP IS ALMOST 20-FEET (6 METERS) LONG AND TOOK OVER ONE TON OF STEEL TO CONSTRUCT. IT WAS MADE IN AMHERST, NOVA SCOTIA, IN 1998 BUT CAN NOW BE FOUND IN BOSTON, MASSACHUSETTS.

However, the type of wire paper clip used by most people today was first produced around 1890 by the Gem Manufacturing Company in Britain, but it was never patented. A Norwegian named Johan Vaaler was granted patents for his design in Germany in 1899 and in the United States (1901), but it never entered production because it was not as successful a design as the "Gem." More recently, the standard wire paper clip's utilitarian design has been jazzed up using colorful coatings.

THE SATELLITE

INVENTORS Russian scientists   **DATE** 1957   **COUNTRY** Russia

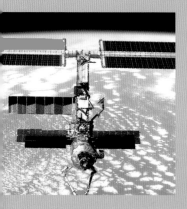

ABOVE The International Space Station, commissioned in November 2000, is the latest manned satellite to orbit the earth.

BELOW RIGHT A technician puts the finishing touches to Sputnik 1, the first artificial satellite to be launched into orbit in 1957.

A satellite is a body that orbits another, larger body in space—the moon is a satellite of the earth, and the planets in our solar system are satellites of the sun.

Within the last 50 years, a new type of satellite has appeared above our planet, the artificial satellite, created and launched by humans from the surface of the earth. Sputnik 1 was the first artificial satellite, and was launched by the USSR on October 4, 1957.

All satellites need to be launched into space using rockets, which accelerate to a speed over 16,780 miles (27,000 kilometers) per hour, so that the satellite can withstand the pull of the earth's gravity, and orbit at an altitude of about 150 miles (240 kilometers).

The satellites that bring us digital television and telecommunications have to maintain "geostationary" orbits; that is, they must remain over a fixed point on the earth's surface. To do this they must complete an orbit in 24 hours so that they are synchronized with the earth's speed of rotation. An orbital height of about 22,370 miles (36,000 kilometers) is required, the satellite maintaining a velocity of about 6,835 miles (11,000 kilometers) per hour—a slower speed is needed the further the object is from the Earth's gravitational pull.

The International Space Station is a satellite. A joint venture between several countries, it provides research facilities in space with a habitable volume of 15,000 cubic feet (425 cubic meters). Russia and America provide the launch capabilities to send cosmonauts or astronauts to the station and return them to earth.

The world's communications now depend on many artificial satellites, including the American GPS satellite network, essential for navigation and position finding, telecommunications, and entertainment from digital satellite television.

IT IS ESTIMATED THAT THERE ARE NOW ABOUT 25,000 MAN-MADE OBJECTS IN ORBIT AROUND THE EARTH, WITH OVER 8,600 FUNCTIONING SATELLITES AND THE REST IN A STATE OF DECAY.

THE COTTON GIN

INVENTOR Eli Whitney   **DATE** 1794   **COUNTRY** USA

A cotton gin is a device designed to separate the fibers from cotton seed pods using a series of teeth to pull the cotton through a wire mesh and brushes to clear any loose cotton fibers.

ABOVE Eli Whitney was credited with the invention in 1793 of the cotton gin. The patent was granted in 1794.

RIGHT A modern automated cotton gin separates the seeds from the cotton.

Although a much more basic device called a "charkha" had been used for this purpose in India for a different type of cotton, the cotton gin (an abbreviation of "engine") was patented in 1794 by Eli Whitney.

The invention of the mechanism enabled cotton plantation owners to massively increase their yield with slave labor—using the basic, hand-driven box gin increased a laborer's output to 50 times that of a laborer working manually. The explosion in the production of cotton in the southern states of America resulted in increased demand for laborers for the work, which was still fiddly and painful, and landowners once again needed slaves to maintain production, a social development that contributed to the American Civil War. Later on the gin was mechanized on a much larger scale, with machines being driven by steam engines. By helping to make the production of textiles possible on a large scale, combined with the developments in the loom and textile production in Britain, the cotton gin helped to fuel the Industrial Revolution.

"THE COTTON GIN NOT ONLY CREATED THE HISTORICAL PATTERNS OF AMERICAN CAPITALISM, IT LAID AN INDELIBLE IMPRESS ON EUROPEAN DEVELOPMENT AS WELL."
C.L.R. JAMES

THE STILETTO HEEL

DESIGNER Roger Vivier **DATE** 1955 **COUNTRY** Italy

A stiletto heel is a tall, slim shoe heel designed to raise the heel of the foot, adding height and elegance to the wearer.

Stiletto heels first appeared on fashion shoes designed by Roger Vivier for Christian Dior in Italy in 1955, and were quickly copied by other shoe designers. They have since become an essential fashion accessory, changing in shape and height many times.

High-heeled shoes are nothing new. They are known to have been worn in ancient Egypt for practical reasons—butchers wore them to raise their feet above the ground and Mongolian horsemen wore heels on their boots to help them grip their stirrups and control their horses. However, it is believed that the first known appearance of the high heel as a fashion accessory was in 1533 when Catherine de Medici of Florence took shoes with two-inch heels with her to France for her marriage to the Duke d'Orleans. At just 14 years old, she was self-conscious about her lack of height, but the shoes immediately became popular with the ladies at the French court, and heels have developed in design and height during the centuries that followed according to fashion.

Tall shoe heels fell out of favor until right up to the 1920s, when the fashion for higher skirt hems resulted in the need for shoes with taller heels

to help display ladies' legs and feet to best effect. The Italian stiletto-heeled shoes of the late 1950s were a natural progression, using reinforced metal rods to support the weight of the wearer.

"STILETTO—I LOOK AT IT MORE AS AN ATTITUDE AS OPPOSED TO A HIGH-HEELED SHOE."
LITA FORD

THE PLAYING CARD

INVENTOR Unknown **DATE** Unknown **COUNTRY** Unknown

Today, the standard pack of 52 cards with four "suits" is used throughout the English-speaking world as the basis for a vast range of popular games, such as bridge, poker, cribbage, and many more, often involving gambling as well as fortune-telling. Although continental European countries use different card designs, many of the card games are similar, if not completely the same.

> ## "CARDS ARE WAR, IN DISGUISE OF A SPORT."
> ### CHARLES LAMB

The precise origin of playing cards is not known. Experts differ as to whether they first appeared in China, India, or Egypt. The earliest European references to playing cards date back to the 1370s and come from Italy, France, Spain, and southern Germany, when the games were introduced by the Arabs.

No cards from this early period survive but literary sources indicate that the cards were handmade, painted in various colors, and even finished in gold. Islamic cards used courtly representations of kings and their entourage, but differences in culture across Europe led to the evolution of a diverse range of playing card types. The French suit system first emerged in the late 1400s, using spades, hearts, diamonds, and clubs, and became the most widely used suit system.

The basic designs have remained the same, but improvements in production processes allowed the paper cards to be coated with plastic to increase their durability.

LEFT The Jack from a French card deck of the revolutionary period, dated 1792.

RIGHT A double-faced King of Clubs from the end of the 19th century.

DURING THE FRENCH REVOLUTION, THE TRADITIONAL DESIGN OF KINGS, QUEENS, AND JACKS WAS OUTLAWED AND REPLACED WITH LIBERTIES, EQUALITIES, AND FRATERNITIES.

THE JET ENGINE

INVENTORS Hans von Ohain and Frank Whittle   **DATE** 1930s   **COUNTRY** Germany and USA

ABOVE The British inventor Frank Whittle patented his jet engine 1930, unaware that the Germans had also developed one.

In the 1920s, a young RAF pilot, Frank Whittle, presented to the Air Ministry a design for a jet engine, which was rejected. Undeterred, Whittle patented his "turbojet engine" in 1930.

Inventors had been working on the concept of jet engines for many years. The main problem was that any engine capable of jet propulsion created too much heat within the chamber, which meant it became unstable and often exploded. Whittle's brilliant but simple solution was to create ten combustion chambers, each of which would produce an impressive thrust, rather than having one large chamber that would produce an uncontrollable reaction.

In 1936, Whittle set up a company called Power Jets Ltd and in 1937, using newly available alloys that were strong and light, he produced a viable engine that worked under laboratory conditions. By 1941 the engine was installed in the prototype of a new jet fighter. The next jet to be made, the Gloster Meteor, was actually used by the RAF in 1944. Unknown to the British, however, a German physicist Hans von Ohain had simultaneously invented a jet engine in Germany. It flew before Whittle's, although it was kept as a military secret in the years before the war.

The jet engine opened up the age of international travel. Its use as a passenger aircraft allowing people to cross the Atlantic at great speed and in greater safety than before was soon recognized. In the 1950s, the American aerospace company Boeing took over the lead in jet-powered airliners. The Boeing 707 entered service in 1958.

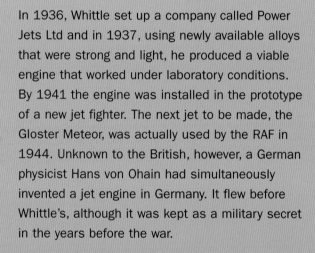

LEFT The Gloster Meteor was the first production airplane to use Whittle's jet engine, and saw action toward the end of World War II.

COMPACT DISCS

INVENTOR James T. Russell   **DATE** 1960s   **COUNTRY** USA

The digital compact disc was invented in the late 1960s by James T. Russell, of Bremerton, Washington. Frustrated by the wear and tear suffered by vinyl records, he began work from his home on a way of creating a system that would record and replay sounds without physical contact between its parts.

RIGHT The lens used to project a laser onto a compact disc.

After years of work, Russell succeeded in inventing the first digital-to-optical recording and playback system, which, as he intended, was immune to the damage suffered by records. The disc, covered with a transparent coating, is read by a laser beam. Since nothing touches the encoded portion, it is not worn out by the playing process. Russell patented his first compact disc in 1970. Through the 1970s, he refined his invention and found ways of adapting it to any form of data. By 1985, Russell had 26 patents for CD-ROM technology and, by 1991, the CD being smaller and of better sound quality than vinyl and audiocassettes, it was the public's number one music carrier.

THE MUSIC ON A COMPACT DISC IS IMPRINTED IN THE FORM OF PITS OF VARYING LENGTH ON A SPIRAL TRACK. THE WIDTH OF THE PITS IS HALF A MICRON—WHICH IS THE DISTANCE A HUMAN HAIR GROWS IN TWO MINUTES AND A FINGERNAIL IN SEVEN MINUTES.

IF YOU STRETCHED ALL THE DATA STORED ON A SINGLE COMPACT DISC INTO A STRAIGHT LINE, IT WOULD REACH OVER FOUR MILES (6.4 KILOMETERS) IN LENGTH.

THE PRINTING PRESS

INVENTOR Johannes Gutenberg   **DATE** 1450   **COUNTRY** Germany

The inventor of the printing press was a German goldsmith, Johannes Gutenberg. His printing press, which was the basic design of the printing press until the late 20th century, was the first to use movable type and oil-based inks and it allowed books to be mass produced for the first time.

Prior to Gutenberg's 1450 invention, books had to be hand copied or wood engraved—both were long and laborious processes. His work as a goldsmith meant that he understood the different qualities of metals. He chose to make his type from an alloy of lead, tin, and antimony; it proved a sound decision and produced high-quality print.

ABOVE One of the priceless copies of the Bible printed by Gutenberg, this one dating from 1456.

One of Gutenberg's most ambitious projects was to print 200 copies of the Bible in 1452. He also printed a small number on vellum as a deluxe edition. The bibles were sold at the 1455 Frankfurt Book Fair, and cost the equivalent of three years' pay for the average clerk. Some fifty Gutenberg bibles survive today.

"THE EASIER IT IS TO COMMUNICATE, THE FASTER CHANGE HAPPENS."

JAMES BURKE, AUTHOR AND SCIENCE HISTORIAN

The Industrial Revolution and the introduction of the steam-powered rotary press allowed thousands of copies of a page to be made in a single day, and the mass production of books flourished. Books soon became cheaper and increasing numbers of people could afford them. More than ever before, new ideas—political, artistic, and social—were disseminated on a grand scale.

THE CATSEYE ROAD REFLECTOR

INVENTOR Percy Shaw   **DATE** 1934   **COUNTRY** UK

The "Catseye" road reflector was invented by Percy Shaw who, after several years developing his design, registered the idea at the British Patent Office in 1934. Shaw had had little education, leaving school at 13 and initially working as a laborer.

He showed early promise of ingenuity, inventing various games and earning money by selling garden produce, and he worked with his father in a forge, which gave him an insight into things mechanical and led him, through repairing items of machinery including road rollers, to set up his own business making paths, drives, and repairing roads.

It is said that the idea for the Catseye came to Shaw when driving at night along dangerous and poorly marked, unlit roads near his home in Yorkshire in northern England, although Shaw himself often said he simply saw road reflectors by the side of the road. He was so convinced of the soundness of his idea that he set up a company, Reflecting Roadstuds Ltd, to manufacture his reflectors. Business was slow at first, but change came when his design won a Transport Department competition in 1937 for a reflecting device to make driving at night safer.

After World War II there was increasing demand and the company expanded rapidly to produce a million Catseyes a year to satisfy home and export demand. Shaw died in 1976, a millionaire.

ABOVE The Catseye is still in use on roads today as an effective way to indicate the centre of the road, and also to indicate the division of lanes.

PERCY SHAW WAS AN ECCENTRIC AND LIVED A QUIET AND FRUGAL LIFE, ESCHEWING LUXURIES, APART FROM HIS BELOVED ROLLS-ROYCE MOTOR CARS. HE WAS ALSO KNOWN TO WATCH THREE OR FOUR TELEVISION SETS SHOWING DIFFERENT PROGRAMS SIMULTANEOUSLY.

ELECTRIC MOTOR

INVENTOR Michael Faraday   **DATE** 1831   **COUNTRY** UK

Almost every mechanical movement we see is caused by an AC or DC electric motor which works by converting electrical energy into mechanical energy. Today, electric motors are found in household appliances such as fans, fridges, washing machines, pool pumps and fan-assisted ovens, and much more.

It was the British scientist Michael Faraday who first discovered the principle of converting electrical energy into mechanical energy by electromagnetic means in 1831. He experimented with a free-hanging wire that dipped into a pool of mercury. A permanent magnet was placed in the middle of the mercury, and when a current was passed through the wire, the wire rotated around the magnet. This showed that the current produced a circular magnetic field around the wire. This type of mechanical energy was known as Direct Current (DC). In 1887, Nikola Tesla introduced the Alternate Current (AC) motor (see page 14). Today, alternate current motors are used more than direct current motors.

An electric motor uses magnets and magnetism to create motion. Magnets work because opposite poles attract and like poles repel. This means that if you have two bar magnets with their ends marked "north" and "south," then the north end of one magnet will attract the south end of the other, and vice versa. Inside an electric motor, these attracting and repelling forces create motion.

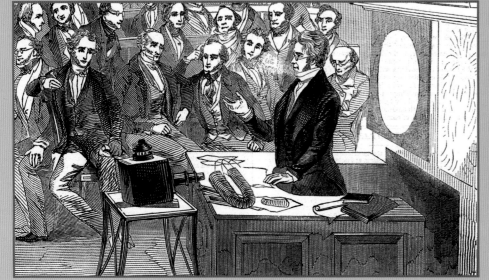

ABOVE LEFT Michael Faraday discovered that it was possible to convert convert electrical energy into mechanical energy using electromagnetism.

LEFT Faraday giving a lecture on electricity and magnetism to the Royal Institution in London in January 1846.

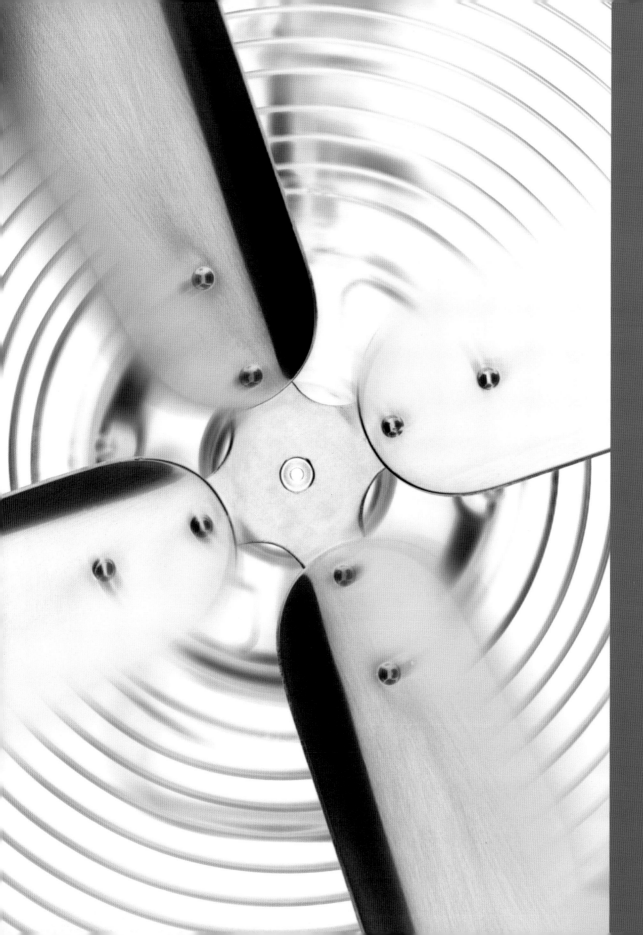

"NOTHING IS TOO
WONDERFUL TO
BE TRUE IF IT BE
CONSISTANT WITH
THE LAWS OF
NATURE."
MICHAEL FARADAY

THE PARACHUTE

INVENTOR Louis Sebastian Lenormand   **DATE** 1783   **COUNTRY** France

ABOVE A late 19th-century illustration of André-Jacques Garnerin releasing his balloon and descending to the ground with the aid of a parachute in 1797.

RIGHT A reconstruction of Leonardi Da Vinci's parachute, taken from the sketches he made in 1485.

A French physicist, Louis Sebastian Lenormand, discovered the principle of the parachute in 1783. His intention was to make a device that allowed people to jump to safety from burning buildings. His first parachute was made from two umbrellas, which he used to jump safely out of a tree.

He called his device a "parachute"; the word comes from the French *parasol* meaning "sun shield," and *chute* meaning "fall."

In 1783 another Frenchman Jean Pierre Blanchard began experimenting with parachutes using his dog, which was placed in a basket attached to the parachute. The first person to jump with a parachute was André-Jacques Garnerin. In 1797 Garnerin attached a parachute to a balloon and, staying in the basket, he released the balloon over the Parc Monceau in Paris at an altitude of 3,000 feet (900 meters). Neither his drop nor his landing steady and, although he was unharmed, it was obvious that the parachute wasn't yet stable. Stability was achieved in 1804 when the French astronomer Lelandes discovered that by cutting a small hole in the apex of the parachute the air pressure was reduced and the oscillations stopped. In 1911 Grant Morton and Captain Albert Berry were the first men to parachute from an airplane.

Originally parachutes were made from canvas. Later silk was used, and then nylon (see page 35).

IN 1485, LEONARDO DA VINCI HAD SKETCHED A MAN FALLING THROUGH THE AIR ATTACHED TO A DEVICE THAT RESEMBLES THE MODERN PARACHUTE.

THE ABACUS

INVENTOR Unknown   **DATE** Unknown   **COUNTRY** Unknown

ABOVE This mosaic from 212 AD depicts a Roman soldier about to kill the Greek mathematician Archmides, who is shown using an abacus.

The abacus is a counting device consisting of a frame with wires along which beads are free to slide. A typical arrangement is to have one or two rows of beads at the top of the frame and five rows of beads at the bottom, sitting flat so that gravity does not control the beads.

Those with two top rows are known as 2/5 and there are variations designated 1/5 and 1/4, the last being used in Japan where it is known as *soroban*.

The abacus has ten columns of beads laterally, signifying, from right to left, one, ten, one hundred, one thousand, etcetera. Separating the top rows from the bottom rows is a bar across which the beads cannot be passed, but with a space so that beads may be moved towards it. Counting is achieved by moving the beads toward this bar and leaving them there so that they are seen as counted.

The abacus evolved from earlier devices used in commerce before written numbers came into use, with the fingers of the hand used for simple calculations. More complex sums required more sophisticated means of counting. Systems using stones and sticks developed into counting boards which were made of stone or wood, with grooves and markers to represent numbers.

An ancient example of a stone counting board survives from the Babylonian period around 300 BCE. In the Chinese chronicles the abacus is first mentioned around 1200 CE, although a similar device was used by the ancient Romans before then.

SOME JAPANESE OPERATORS OF THE ABACUS CAN CALCULATE SUMS AS RAPIDLY AS USERS OF ELECTRONIC CALCULATORS.

JEANS

INVENTORS Jacob Davis, Levi Strauss   **DATE** 1873 Blue Jeans   **COUNTRY** USA   **PATENTED** 1873

Possibly the most iconic item of clothing of the 20th century, jeans originated in the USA. They were invented in 1873 by two immigrants, Jacob Davis and Levi Strauss, though workmen had worn trousers known as "waist overalls" for decades.

ABOVE An American advertising handbill from 1899 promoting Levi Strauss jeans and their various applications.

The waist overalls were made of denim, a cotton twill material dyed blue with indigo. The problem with them was that the pockets were too easily ripped. Jacob Davis, a Latvian tailor living in Nevada, came up with the idea of using rivets on the pockets to strengthen them. Needing a business partner, he contacted dry-goods wholesaler Levi Strauss and together they filed for and received the patent for "Fastening Pocket-Openings" in 1873. Around 1890, the trousers were assigned the number 501, which they still bear today. For nearly 20 years, Levi Strauss & Co. was the only company allowed to make riveted clothing. When the patent expired numerous companies began to make cotton jeans with rivets.

THE WORD "DENIM" PROBABLY CAME FROM THE NAME OF A FRENCH MATERIAL "SERGE DE NÎMES"—SERGE IS A TYPE OF FABRIC.

X-RAYS

INVENTOR Wilhelm Conrad Röntgen   **DATE** 1895   **COUNTRY** Germany

X-rays are electromagnetic waves of short wavelength, capable of penetrating a thickness of matter. They were discovered quite by accident in 1895 by Wilhelm Conrad Röntgen, a professor of physics in Germany.

RIGHT An early X-ray, taken in India in 1897, clearly shows the finger bones in a hand.

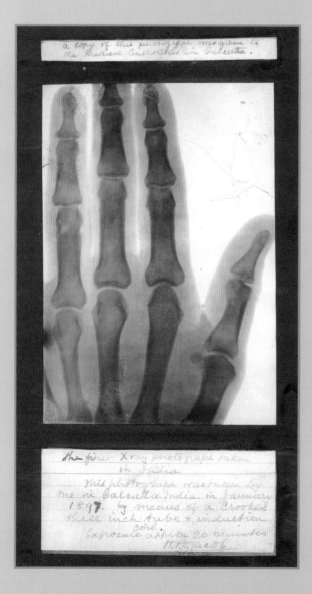

Röntgen was performing experiments with a Crookes tube. Named for its inventor, the British physicist Sir William Crookes, the tube produced streams of electrons, called cathode rays. Before going to lunch one day, Röntgen put the activated tube on a book. What he didn't notice was that there was a key lying on a piece of photographic film inside the book. When he later developed the film, he discovered the image of the key—Röntgen had accidentally taken the first X-ray. A week after his discovery, he took an X-ray photograph of his wife's hand which clearly revealed her wedding ring and her bones.

This new form of radiation was X-radiation (X standing for "Unknown"), abbreviated to X-ray. Its immediate importance was that it allowed diagnosis of skeletal disease and damage without the need for exploratory surgery.

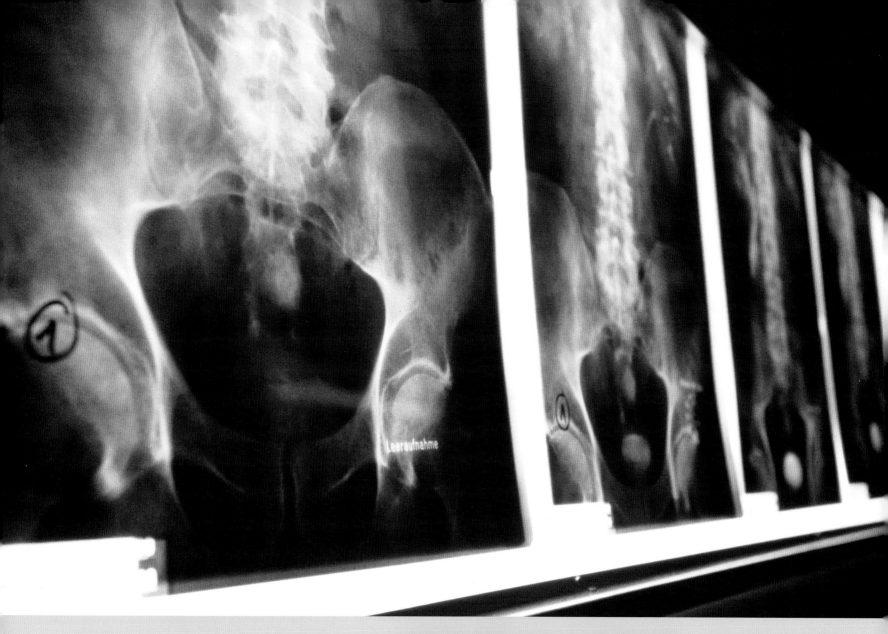

Different tissues in the body absorb X-rays at different rates. For example, calcium in bones absorbs X-rays the most, so bones look white on an X-ray image (radiograph). Fat and other soft tissues absorb less, and look gray. Air absorbs the least, so lungs appear black on a radiograph.

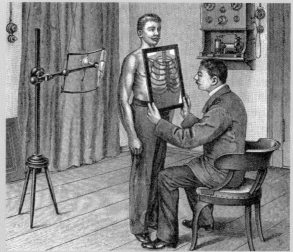

LEFT The X-ray tube being used to examine a patient in Germany in 1903. The patient stands in front of the tube and the doctor holds up a specially coated screen to view the patient's ribs.

PAPER

INVENTOR Unknown   **DATE** Unknown   **COUNTRY** Unknown

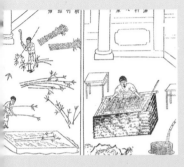

ABOVE An illustration from China showing the ancient process of paper-making.

Paper is essentially a mass of natural fibers, processed to bind together, then pressed to form a thin, flat surface for writing or printing on. It is difficult today to imagine life without paper; millions of tons of it are produced every year. Books, magazines, and newspapers are just a few of its many uses.

Paper has a long history, its name deriving from the papyrus reed that grows along the River Nile, and was used by the ancient Egyptians to make a writing material from about 3000 BCE. It was also used by the ancient Greeks and Romans.

The first written record of paper-making as we know it today comes from China. In 105 CE, a chronicle records that a court official called Ts'ai Lun invented paper from recycling rags.

Papermaking became highly developed in China to satisfy the demands of a growing bureaucracy. It then spread from China to Korea and Japan, where the art of making it by hand persists to this day. The techniques spread to Arabia and thence to Europe via Italy.

The use of water-driven mills to make paper, by a process of hammering the pulp onto a felt base, began in Germany and spread throughout Europe in the 16th century. This industrial process was necessary to meet the growing demand. At about this time a shortage of raw materials started to inhibit production, and this was not properly resolved until the mid-19th century with the introduction of ground-up wood to the industry. Now various chemical processes are used to produce differing grades of paper for its many applications.

LEFT An ancient Egyptian papyrus copy of the *Book of the Dead*.

THE FIRST RECORDED PRINTED NEWS REPORT IN A FORMAT PERHAPS RECOGNIZABLE AS A NEWSPAPER IS BELIEVED TO HAVE APPEARED IN 1605, PUBLISHED IN GERMANY BY JOHANN CAROLUS.

THE **CAMERA**

INVENTOR Joseph Nicephore Niépce **DATE** 1826 **COUNTRY** France

The word "photography" is derived from the Greek words "photos," meaning light, and "graphein," to draw. It is the method of recording images by the action of light on a light-sensitive material.

ABOVE A daguerrotype of the photographic process's own inventor, Louis Jacque Daguerre, made in 1846.

RIGHT The very first photograph, taken by Joseph Nicephore Niépce in 1826 of the view through a window.

It is thought that an Iraqi scientist invented the camera obscura in the 11th century. The camera obscura worked by using a pinhole to project an image onto a viewing surface. There was no way of preserving these images though.

The first photograph was taken by Joseph Nicephore Niépce in 1826. At the same time, fellow Frenchman Louis Jacques Mandé Daguerre, who is considered the first inventor of practical photography, was experimenting with the effects of light upon translucent paintings.

Daguerre formed a partnership with Niépce and together they worked on improving the process that Niépce had begun in 1826. Success came with the "daguerreotype," named for Daguerre. He coated a copper plate with silver and treated it with iodine to make it light sensitive. The image was developed by mercury vapor and fixed with a strong solution of salt.

American photographers were thrilled by the daguerrotype, which enabled them to capture a good likeness of the sitter. Soon there were

daguerreotypists in all the major cities of the USA, all hoping to be able to photography the politicians and celebrities of the day.

Photographic film was developed by George Eastman, who began manufacturing film made of paper in 1885 and film made of celluloid in 1889. His first camera, the Kodak, was manufactured in 1888. Photography really took off, however, with Eastman's "Box Brownie" which went on sale in 1900 and remained popular up into the 1960s.

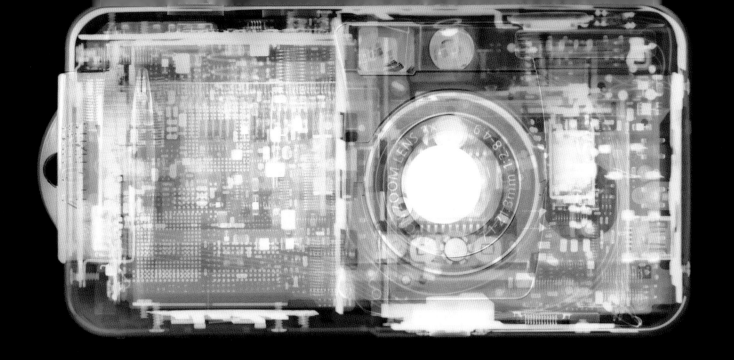

BY 1850, THERE WERE OVER 70 DAGUERREOTYPE STUDIOS IN NEW YORK CITY ALONE. THEIR POPULARITY DECLINED IN THE 1850S WHEN THE AMBROTYPE, A FASTER AND LESS EXPENSIVE PROCESS BECAME AVAILABLE.

THE SKI LIFT

INVENTOR Gerhard Mueller   **DATE** 1930   **COUNTRY** Germany

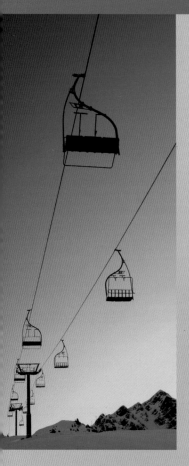

The term "ski lift" mostly refers to the type of chair lift seen at mountain resorts around the world. In essence, these chair lifts consist of an endless loop of wire rope or cable wound around grooved wheels at each end of the system, one at the top of the mountain and one at the bottom.

One of these wheels is driven, usually by electric motor. The cables are supported by rollers that sit on towers set along the length of the run. The chairs with between two and four seats are suspended from the cables. The lift is driven at a constant speed which must be slow enough to enable skiers to get on and off without danger.

A variant of this basic design allows the clamps by which the chairs are attached to the cable to "declutch," or slip at each end of the run. With this design much faster running speeds can be achieved, but the chairs are able to slow to allow safer mounting and dismounting at each end.

There are other means of transport to the tops of ski slopes or mountains, including the gondola lift (passenger cars attached to cables in similar ways to chair lifts) and funicular railways, which use coaches running on rails attached to cables. Comprehensive safety and braking systems must be fitted to all of these systems, which are developments of mechanical ropeways used in Europe since the 17th century.

The invention of the ski lift shortly after 1930 is credited to Gerhard Mueller, a German engineer who created the world's first rope tow using parts of a motorbike and some rope. In 1934, Erich Constam built the first proper drag lift, and by the end of the 1930s the world's first chair lift had opened at Sun Valley in Idaho.

ABOVE A chair lift in the mountains, designed to take skiers to the top of a ski slope.

THE MOST BIZARRELY SITUATED SKI LIFT IN THE WORLD IS ON THE SLOPES OF MOUNT ETNA, AN ACTIVE VOLCANO IN SICILY.

BRAILLE

INVENTOR Louis Braille   **DATE** 1827   **COUNTRY** France

Braille is a system of "printing" text, using symbols consisting of raised or embossed dots, designed to enable blind and partially sighted people to read and write. Braille text represents letters of the alphabet and punctuation marks; the reader feels the dots, usually with the index fingers of both hands.

Over the years a number of systems had been explored to help blind people to read, many of them simply using raised versions of normal typeset letters. Louis Braille injured his eye at the age of three in 1812 and, following a series of ineffective treatments, infection set in and spread, leaving him blind. In 1821, at the National Institute for the Blind in Paris, Braille came into contact with a secret military code, called night writing, which had been invented to help soldiers communicate in battle after dark. Braille developed and refined the system using a basic cell of six dots, from which he developed a set of symbols, so that a person could read each cell with one fingertip. The first book printed using Braille's system was published in 1827. After his initial struggles to get his system accepted, braille is now used throughout the world and remains basically as he invented it. Recent refinements have contracted groups of letters and common words to increase the speed of reading, and to reduce the size and cost of braille books.

ABOVE Louis Braille, who became blind as the result of an injury, developed a practical system enabling blind people to read that is still in use today.

The invention of braille has enabled the blind and partially sighted to access a vast range of reading material that sighted people take for granted, including bank statements, insurance policies, playing cards, and music.

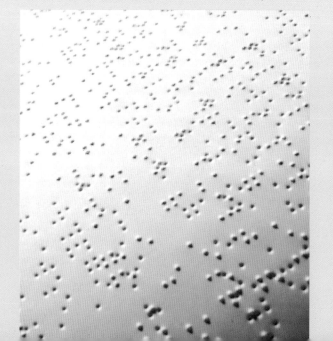

"THERE IS A WONDER IN READING BRAILLE THAT THE SIGHTED WILL NEVER KNOW: TO TOUCH WORDS AND HAVE THEM TOUCH YOU BACK."
JIM FIEBIG

THE EJECTOR SEAT

INVENTOR Junkers   **DATE** 1939   **COUNTRY** Germany

The ejector seat is designed to propel a pilot and other crew members away from the cockpit of an aircraft during an emergency and return them safely to the ground using a parachute.

ABOVE In 1954 the US Air Force tests its ejector seat as a pilot is ejected from a B-47 jet bomber at an altitude of 10,000 feet.

The first aircraft escape systems consisted simply of parachutes, which were issued to pilots during World War I. The British Royal Air Force actually stopped their pilots using parachutes as they thought it would encourage them to abandon their craft at crucial moments. The German Air Force immediately saw the importance of protecting their valuable air crews, however, and distributed parachutes widely to their pilots.

At the start of World War II, as the performance of military aircraft increased substantially and it became far more difficult for a pilot to jump clear, the Germans began to develop systems to propel a pilot safely away from a stricken airplane, firstly by using spring mechanisms, but later using compressed air.

The first patent for an aircraft ejector seat was granted to the aircraft manufacturer Junkers in 1939, with a subsequent patent granted for the additional use of a power cartridge. Heinkel developed the ejector seat, and the first working seat was fitted to the prototype Heinkel 176. The first use of a production ejector seat was on January 13, 1943, when a pilot called Schenke ejected from his failing Heinkel He-280. By 1944 Heinkel had begun to use explosive charges to eject the seats out of cockpits.

Since the war, the British company Martin-Baker has led development of automatic ejector seats for military jet aircraft. Systems for large passenger aircraft are still considered to be too heavy and expensive for introduction.

THE MOST FAMOUS USE OF AN EJECTOR SEAT IS PROBABLY A FICTIONAL ONE. IN THE 1965 MOVIE *GOLDFINGER*, SECRET AGENT JAMES BOND USES AN EJECTOR SEAT FITTED TO HIS ASTON MARTIN DB5 CAR TO DISPOSE OF AN UNWANTED PASSENGER.

BELOW In 1993 this Russian Mig-29 526 crashed after colliding with a Mig-29 925 at the Fairford airshow in the UK. Both pilots ejected and survived.

THE TELESCOPE

INVENTOR Jan Lippershey   **DATE** 1608   **COUNTRY** Holland

Amazingly, the modern telescope is still largely based on the design of Sir Isaac Newton's telescope invented in 1704. Up to this time, telescopes had used an arrangement of glass lenses to magnify objects. Newton's design was different: it used a curved mirror to take in and reflect light. This proved more powerful and gave the user a greater field of vision.

ABOVE In July 1609, Galileo Galilei was in Venice, when he heard of an invention that allowed distant objects to be seen as clearly as if they were nearby. This inspired him to invent his own telecope.

The first patent application for a telescope was in October, 1608, from Jan Lippershey, an eyeglass maker in modern Holland. Lippershey was employed as the official telescope maker for his country.

It was Galileo Galilei who introduced the telescope to astronomy in 1609. Galileo was the first man to see the craters of the moon, sunspots, the four large moons of Jupiter, and the rings of Saturn. His telescope provided limited magnification—up to 30 times—and a narrow field of view. He could only see a quarter of the moon's face at any one time.

The world's largest telescope is the Binocular Telescope located on Mount Graham in Arizona. It is the most technologically advanced ground-based telescope in the world. Its mirrors are much larger and lighter than conventional solid-glass mirrors and collect more light than any other existing telescope. Its creators say that it will enable the measurement of objects dating back to the beginning of time.

ABOVE The English scientist and mathematician Isaac Newton's revolutionary reflecting telescope.

THE ATM

INVENTOR Luther Simijian   **DATE** 1939   **COUNTRY** USA

Can any of us remember a time when we had to stick to banking hours to cash a cheque? It was the inconvenience of this system that led John Shepherd-Barron to invent the first electronic ATM (automated teller machine) in the 1960s.

RIGHT Todays ATMs don't just dispense cash: they can give you your account balance, make cash advances to your credit card and allow you to top-up your cell phone.

His ATM was installed in London in 1967 by Barclays Bank, though an earlier version of the ATM had existed. Invented by a lifelong innovator, Turkish-born Luther George Simjian, this was a mechanical cash dispenser installed in New York by the City Bank of New York 1939, but it was never popular with the public.

To begin with, bankers were not very excited about ATMs, since the annual cost of one machine was some $8,000 higher than the cost of a human bank clerk. And—since the first ATMs were offline devices not connected by a computer network to clients' account—the banks only allowed clients with good banking records to use the new service. Today's sophisticated ATMs have come to be recognized as one of the great conveniences of modern life—and whether in Alaska or Adelaide, you can take out money from a "hole in the wall."

THE IDEA OF A PERSONAL IDENTIFICATION NUMBER (PIN) WAS DEVELOPED BY THE BRITISH ENGINEER JAMES GOODFELLOW IN 1965.

THE BOW AND ARROW

INVENTOR Unknown DATE Unknown COUNTRY Unknown

A bow consists of a curved piece of wood with a taut, springy string attached to each end. Placing an arrow across the center of the bow and using the bowstring to propel the arrow creates a basic but very effective weapon.

The origin of the bow is not known for certain, but there exists evidence as far back as 50,000 years ago, in the form of flint arrow heads. Bows made from wood or bone have been dated to about 9,000 years old.

The Egyptians and Assyrians perfected the use of the bow and arrow in battle, fired from chariots or horseback as well as the ground. The crossbow, which uses a cog mechanism to pull the bowstring taut, is believed to have been invented in China somewhere between 500 and 2000 BCE. The weapon was also used by the Greeks and Romans.

In medieval times, the English developed the so-called longbow as their main weapon of war, though it is said to have originated from the type of bow used by the Welsh to fight the English. The longbow was used to great effect at the battle of Crécy in 1346 where an outnumbered English force prevailed over French and Genoese troops, mainly because the longbow could loose several arrows to the crossbow's one. The English longbow, made of yew, was the pinnacle of weapon development at that time, although later improvements like laminated bows provided more power.

LEFT This pre-historic carving found on Newspaper Rock State Historic Monument, Utah, shows a horseman hunting elk using a bow and arrow.

BELOW Archery, once the preserve of hunters and fighters, is now a precision sport.

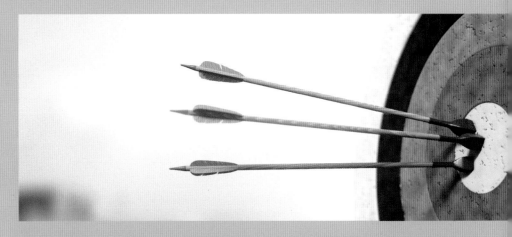

IN THE 16TH CENTURY IT WAS OBLIGATORY FOR MALES OF MILITARY AGE IN ENGLAND TO BE TAUGHT TO USE THE LONGBOW.

THE HOLOGRAM

INVENTOR Dennis Gabor **DATE** 1947 **COUNTRY** Hungary

The word "hologram" derives from the Greek "holos," meaning whole, and "graphe," meaning writing. A hologram is a two-dimensional image that looks three-dimensional under certain conditions.

The inventor of the hologram was a Hungarian physicist, Dennis Gabor. In 1947 he received a patent but, due to the poor quality of the hologram and the fact that Gabor had little idea how to advance the technique, the science of holography didn't develop until the invention of the laser beam in 1960. The first holograms, depicting a bird and a train, were made by Emmett Leith and Juris Upatneiks at the University of Michigan in 1963.

A photograph uses a lens to focus an image on a piece of film and then records where there is light or no light. Holography is a photographic technique that uses the wave nature of light (since light is an electromagnetic wave). When waves of light meet they form an "interference pattern" in the same way that a stone thrown into water will make a pattern in the water. Holography is a record of the interference pattern made by the interaction of two beams of light.

There are several different types of hologram. Transmission holograms are viewed by shining a laser light through them and looking at the reconstructed image from the side of the hologram opposite the source. The rainbow transmission uses white light as a source of illumination. This type of hologram is found on credit cards and passports.

THE ASPIRIN

DISCOVERER Hermann Kolbe   **DATE** 1859   **COUNTRY** Germany

In the 4th or 5th century BCE, Hippocrates, known as the "Father of Medicine," refers to records of the bark and leaves of willow (Salix) being used for pain relief. There is also evidence from Sumerian inscriptions that willow leaves were used to treat rheumatism and the ancient Egyptians were aware of their prophylactic use.

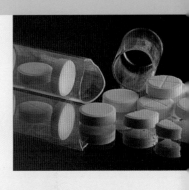

ABOVE In recent years, aspirin's reputation as a "wonder drug" has been reinforced by the discovery that is is very effective as an anti-coagulant, preventing strokes and heart attacks.

In 1763 in England, Edward Stone, a vicar from Oxfordshire, mentioned in correspondence that he had treated sufferers from fever with a solution of willow bark. It wasn't until the 19th century that scientists discovered the active ingredient in willow and called it salicin, after the Latin name for the tree. Various extraction processes were developed to increase the yield and degree of refinement.

In 1859 Hermann Kolbe, a professor of chemistry at Marburg University in Germany, managed to discover the chemical structure of salicin and synthesize it. It could then be produced on an industrial scale. Salicin, or salicylic acid, although effective in pain relief, is also a severe stomach irritant. In 1897 Felix Hoffman, working for the German chemical and pharmaceutical company Bayer, produced a new variant called acetylsalicylic acid which acted as an effective analgesic and anti-inflammatory drug without harming the stomach.

The first synthetic drug was produced by Bayer, to which the trade name "aspirin" was given, and it was soon in mass production. After World War I Bayer were deprived of the right to the trademark and aspirin became the generic name.

ASPIRIN IS THE SINGLE MOST USEFUL ALL-PURPOSE PAINKILLER.

THE CHRONOMETER

INVENTOR John Harrison **DATE** 1961 **COUNTRY** UK

The term chronometer applies to a clock or watch that meets strict standards of accurate timekeeping.

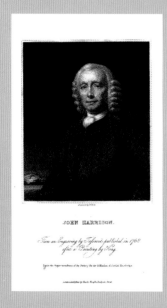

JOHN HARRISON.

From an Engraving by Tassaert published in 1768 after a Painting by King

ABOVE It took John Harrison nearly 30 years of experimentation before he was able to create a clock that was accurate enough to be used at sea.

RIGHT John Harrison's sketches showing the inner workings of his mechanical clock.

In the 17th century, the importance of being able to read time with great accuracy became essential to navigation at sea. Sailors were unable to measure longitude with sufficient accuracy to pinpoint their position, but it had been calculated that, for every additional 15 degrees of longitude, the time changed by an additional one hour. It was therefore understood that if an accurate form of measuring time could be carried on board a vessel, the time could be used to determine the ship's position.

Although accurate pendulum clocks existed (see page 102), the motion of a ship would adversely affect the pendulum's movement. So, in 1675 King Charles II founded the Royal Observatory at Greenwich with the specific purpose of finding an answer to this problem. With increased international competition for control of the seas, the British Government deemed it in the national interest to find a solution and offered a prize of

£20,000 in 1714. The problem was solved by John Harrison, a carpenter from Lincolnshire, who made a series of metal clocks, each demonstrating a greater standard of accuracy. His fourth—H4, a much smaller clock than the others and made for him by a watchmaker—was so successful that it underwent sea trials in 1761. H4 exceeded the requirements to win the prize, and was copied by Larcum Kendall for use at sea (known as K1), but Harrison made an improved version, H5, which lost less than 5 seconds in 10 days.

Today, mechanical clocks and watches are less accurate than their quartz, radio-controlled, or radioactive counterparts, but they still represent a triumph of engineering in miniature.

"OUR FAITHFUL GUIDE THROUGH ALL THE VICISSITUDES OF CLIMATES."

CAPTAIN JAMES COOK ON K1, LARCUM KENDALL'S COPY OF HARRISON'S H4 CLOCK.

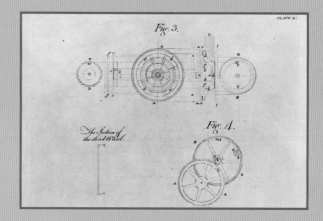

THE SWISS CONTRÔLE OFFICIEL SUISSE DES CHRONOMÈTRES (COSC) TESTS INDIVIDUAL MECHANICAL WATCH MOVEMENTS, ONLY GRANTING THEM OFFICIAL CHRONOMETER STATUS IF THEY MEET THE COSC'S PRECISION CRITERIA OF BETWEEN –4 AND +6 SECONDS PER DAY—FAR LESS ACCURATE THAN HARRISION'S H5.

THE CELL PHONE

INVENTOR AT&T   **DATE** 1978   **COUNTRY** USA

The very first cell phones were really car phones, and initially they were one-way systems. In 1921 the Detroit Police Department began experimenting with a one-way mobile service in their cars, and by 1928 the same police force had one-way radio communication with all its patrol cars.

Things had developed by 1946, when on June 17 a driver in St. Louis pulled out a handset from under his car's dashboard, placed a phone call, and made history. It was the first mobile telephone call. The phone worked off the power from the car's engine and needed an antenna in the car roof. It had taken a team from AT&T Bell Laboratories over a decade to achieve this feat. By 1948, wireless telephone service was available in almost 100 American cities and highway corridors. However, the early mobile phone system suffered from high amounts of line interference.

The real breakthrough came with "cellular" technology. In 1978, AT&T began testing a mobile telephone system based on hexagonal geographical regions called "cells." As the caller's vehicle passed from one cell to another, an automatic switching system would transfer the telephone call to another cell without interruption. The cellular telephone system began nationwide usage in the USA in 1983.

In the 1990s truly portable phones began to emerge. Compact, light-weight, and using long-life batteries, these phones were instantly popular with the public. Cell phones became a status symbol—the smaller the better. Soon cell phone accessories were being manufactured: headsets, ringtones, and iPod adapters all now have a place in modern culture.

ABOVE These cell phones range from the 1980s through to the 21st century. As the years progress, new technology allows the phones to get smaller and smaller.

THE AIRBAG

INVENTOR John Hetrick   **DATE** 1953   **COUNTRY** USA

An airbag, also know as a supplementary restraint system (SRS), is a device designed to protect the chest and head of an occupant of a vehicle involved in a collision. It consists of an expandable membrane that is inflated at high speed by a blast of gas when a device detects the sudden deceleration of the vehicle.

RIGHT Of any vehicle safety product, the airbag has had the most beneficial impact on passenger safety.

The first ground vehicle airbag was patented by John Hetrick in the USA in 1953, and it followed similar devices for aircraft that had been developed in the 1940s. Finding a way to trigger the device was a technical challenge that was solved when another American, Allen Breed, developed a sensor—consisting of a ball in a tube—that detected the vehicle's sudden deceleration. In 1967, he offered his sensor to the Chrysler company.

At first, the device was developed in America as an alternative to the seatbelt in cars, because there was a great deal of resistance among the public in the 1970s to wearing seatbelts. Ford experimented with the device in prototype vehicles from 1971, and General Motors followed from 1973, when they also offered them for sale as an option on their Buick, Cadillac, and Oldsmobile models, but production stopped in 1976 when there were fears over the safety of airbags.

Mercedes-Benz introduced a refined version of the airbag as an option for its expensive S-Class model in 1980, and in 1987 Porsche became the first car manufacturer to fit driver and passenger airbags as standard to its 944 model. Since then, front airbags have become mandatory in many countries, and manufacturers have also developed similar devices to protect vehicle occupants in side collisions.

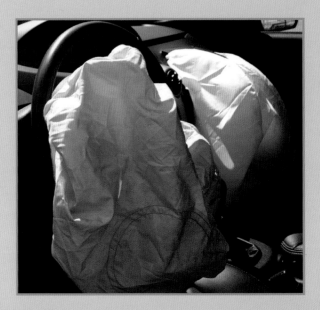

HONDA INTRODUCED THE FIRST AIRBAG FOR MOTORCYCLES IN 2006 ON THEIR GOLDWING MODEL.

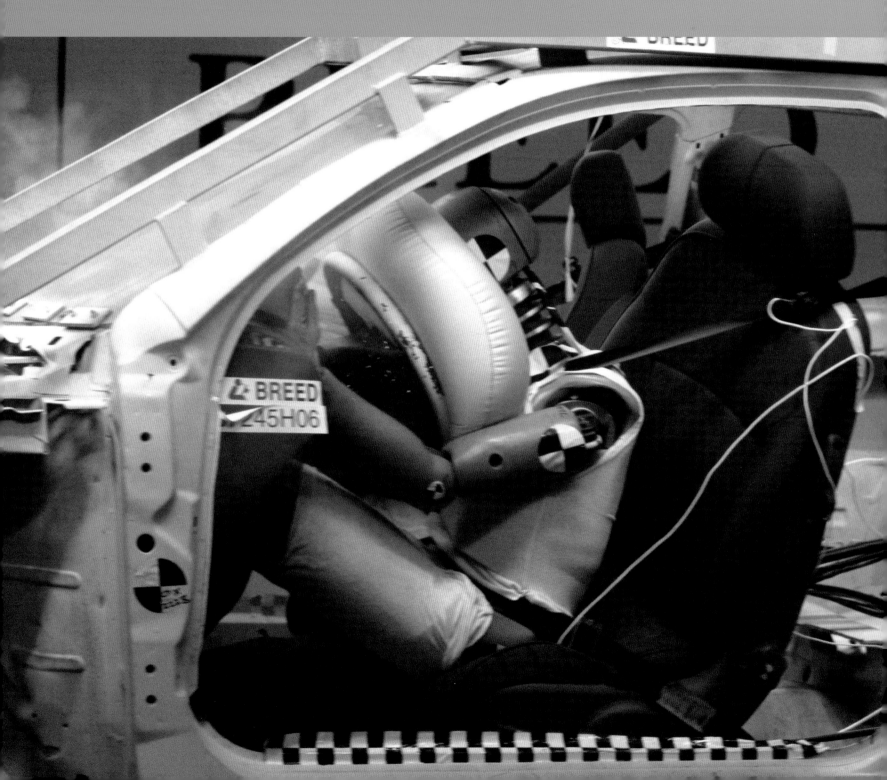

THE NEWSPAPER

INVENTOR Unknown **DATE** 16th century **COUNTRY** Germany

ABOVE It was the invention of the printing press in Germany in the 16th century by goldsmith Johannes Gutenberg (1400–1468) that led to the mass production and circulation of newspapers. The first "newspapers" were really only pamphlets, which often reported news of witchcraft or executions.

The ancient Romans used information sheets, usually to convey opinions or the edicts of rulers, written by hand and placed in prominent positions to be read by the populace. The Chinese used similar handwritten sheets from the 6th century CE.

The first printed "newspapers," pamplets of printed type, which published news and were circulated by hand, arrived in Germany in the 16th century, following the invention of the printing press by Johannes Gutenberg (see page 64). These were essentially propaganda leaflets of a sensational nature.

In the 17th century, newspapers were heavily censored and anything considered to be detrimental to governments, or the ruling classes, was not permitted. Sweden was the first country to pass laws to ensure the freedom of the press in 1766.

The invention of the telegraph system in the mid-19th century revolutionized communication and news gathering—events in distant places could be in print within hours rather than weeks. Between 1890 and 1920, newspapers were the prime source of news and information. The advent of radio in the 1920s and, subsequently, television and the internet have since taken their toll, and readership is in decline.

"A NEWSPAPER IS LUMBER MADE MALLEABLE. IT IS INK MADE INTO WORDS AND PICTURES. IT IS CONCEIVED, BORN, GROWS UP AND DIES OF OLD AGE IN A DAY."

JIM BISHOP

THE LAVA® LAMP

INVENTOR Edward Craven Walker   **DATE** 1960s   **COUNTRY** UK

A Lava® lamp is a distinctively shaped novelty light containing colorful, slowly moving and changing shapes, apparently imitating the motion of molten lava.

ABOVE Edward Craven Walker perfected his secret Lava recipe of oil, wax and other solids in the 1960s. The original model had a large gold base with tiny holes, which simulated starlight. It had a 52-ounce globe that contained red or white Lava and yellow or blue liquid.

The lamp consists of a light bulb at the base of a shaped glass tube, which is filled with a transparent oil and colored blobs of wax. When the light is turned on, the heat of the bulb warms the oil and wax. The wax, being slightly denser than oil when cool, becomes less dense than the oil when they are warm, and so it rises up through the oil, cools toward the top of the lamp and then falls again, creating moving, changing shapes.

Invented as the "Astro Lamp" in the 1960s by Edward Craven Walker, an Englishman, it was spotted at a Hamburg trade show in 1965 by Adolph Wertheimer who bought the American rights to the product and marketed it as the "Lava Lite"®.

The lamp exploded in popularity and became a key style icon of the 1960s, its colorful display reflecting the space-age "psychedelia" of the period. Mr. Walker sold his rights to the lamp in the 1990s to the Mathmos company, which continues to make Lava lamps.

THE MOTION PICTURE

INVENTOR Louis Lumière (and others)   **DATE** 1890s   **COUNTRY** France

In the early 1800s various devices, such as the Zoetrope or Praxinoscope, were designed that animated a series of drawn pictures by rotating them quickly in front of the viewer. Drawn images were soon replaced by photographs taken using the new medium of film, being developed by William Henry Fox Talbot and Jacques Daguerre.

ABOVE This depiction of the Man in the Moon is taken from the 1914 film *A Trip to the Moon*, directed by George Melies.

RIGHT *The Jazz Singer*, released in 1927 was the first motion picture to have sound. Starring Al Jolson, it has the first, and possibly most famous words, in movie history. After hearing Jolson sing, movie-goers heard him say "Wait a minute! Wait a minute! You ain't heard nothin' yet".

France developed the Cinématographie which projected film onto a screen for an audience to watch. Short films made by Georges Méliès in France (*Cinderella* in 1899 and *A Trip to the Moon* in 1902) and by Edwin Porter at Edison's studio in the USA (*The Great Train Robbery* in 1903) pioneered the art form using camera tricks and editing to tell a story. Viewing theaters were rapidly being built to show the new films and satisfy the massive public interest.

However, Thomas Edison's experiments, mostly undertaken by his assistant William K.L. Dickon, led to the patenting of the Kinetoscope in 1891. This device enabled a strip of 50 feet (15 meters) of film to be looped in front of a viewfinder. In 1895, the brothers Louis and Auguste Lumière in

The next great technical step in motion pictures was sound, which was first introduced with the film *The Jazz Singer* in 1927, and subsequently refined with the Movietone system, which allowed sound to be added directly to the film, making it easily synchronized with the pictures.

"THE ART OF MOTION PICTURES IS PICTORIAL AND LANGUAGE COMES A DISTANT SECOND."
JEAN-JACQUES ANNAUD

Although the film studios had experimented with color since 1906, the advent of Technicolor in 1933 led to a huge increase in color film releases. By the end of the 1950s, virtually all motion pictures were being produced in color.

"MOTION PICTURES ARE THE ART FORM OF THE 20TH CENTURY, AND ONE OF THE REASONS IS THE FACT THAT FILMS ARE A SLIGHTLY CORRUPTED ART FORM."
ROGER CORMAN

THE WINDMILL

INVENTOR Persians   **DATE** 7th century   **COUNTRY** Persia

The earliest references to windmills come from Persia in the 7th century, from where they spread to Europe in the 12th century. These devices, designed to harness the power of the wind to turn a mechanism, were extensively used, in Holland and in East Anglia in Great Britain.

BELOW The engraving, *Windmills in Motion*, was produced circa 1580 by Theodoor Galle, after a painting by Flemish artist Joannes Stradanus.

These early windmills were used to pump water to drain the polders and fens, and elsewhere to grind corn for making flour. At one time they would have been an integral part of the landscape in many countries; the few that remain are a reminder of a past technological age.

There are two basic designs of windmill. The first examples were "post mills," which were made of wood, and where the whole body of the mill, mounted on a bearing, had to be manually turned to face the wind. This developed into the "smock mill," the shape resembling an item of clothing worn in the Middle Ages. In this later design, the body of the mill was fixed and could be much larger, with the top of the mill, carrying the rotating arms or sails, sitting on a bearing so that only that part could rotate. The smock mills were followed by tower mills where the body was brick- or stone-built. There was much development of these basic designs in England and Holland, mostly to the arrangements for rotating the head. The addition of a fantail or vane on the other side of the mill head to the sails allowed the sails to be automatically turned into the wind.

The Briton William Cubitt (born in 1785) invented a self-regulating sail by means of weights working against the force of the wind, opening up the shutters in the sail as the wind speed increased. This was patented in 1807 and became standard.

WINDMILLS WERE
SUPERSEDED BY
STEAM AND ELECTRIC
POWER OWING TO THE
UNRELIABILITY OF WIND
AS A POWER SOURCE,
BUT THE WINDMILL
IS UNDERGOING A
RESURGENCE IN THE
FORM OF WIND TURBINES
DESIGNED TO GENERATE
ELECTRICITY FROM
WIND POWER.

THE DIVING SUIT

INVENTOR Augustus Siebe   **DATE** 1837   **COUNTRY** UK

ABOVE In this 1870 illustration a diver is being assisted into a Siebe-Gorman diving suite in preparation to dive. Air would have been pumped down from the surface through a hose that was attached to a copper helmet.

Until the invention of the diving suit, the only way to spend time underwater was to hold one's breath. Pearl fishers in the Far East learned how to hold their breath and stay under the sea for surprisingly long periods.

Aristotle is said to have described a diving device that we would recognize as a diving bell (an upturned vessel that trapped air and allowed an occupant to breathe underwater) in the 4th century BCE. Leonardo da Vinci (1452–1519) left drawings of an apparatus with tubes leading from a float on the water's surface connected to the mask below. Diving bells of more advanced design were made and used between the 16th and 19th centuries when the limit of this design was reached.

However, there was still no safe way for a solitary diver to be mobile enough to work underwater until the first really practical diving suit was available. This started life as a helmet for firemen, designed by English inventor Charles Dean in 1824, to allow them to breathe in smoke-filled buildings. A hose supplied air to the helmet. Augustus Siebe, an engineer living in London, realized that the fire helmet could be adapted for diving. It was a success and was used for many dives. The full diving dress was developed in 1837, with the help of one George Edwards and manufactured by Siebe Gorman & Company (Gorman was Siebe's son-in-law).

"Free" or snorkel and scuba (an acronym of Self-Contained Underwater Breathing Apparatus) diving developed in parallel with the diving suit, snorkels being used since the 4th century in China. Early snorkels were probably no more than a piece of bamboo held in the mouth, allowing the user to breathe without lifting his head: modern versions are made of plastic with a silicone mouthpiece. Scuba divers carry their own air supply in the form of compressed air cylinders. This equipment does not allow immersions of very long duration.

ANESTHETIC

INVENTOR James Simpson   **DATE** 1847   **COUNTRY** UK

Before the discovery of a truly effective anesthetic in the 1840s, surgery was a grim business. In order to spare patients the excruciating pain of operations, surgeons worked as quickly as possible, often making terrible mistakes and losing patients on the operating table.

One of the first effective anesthetics to be discovered was "laughing gas," or nitrous oxide. Sir Humphry Davy (inventor of the miner's lamp) discovered the anesthetizing properties of "laughing gas" in the 1790s. However, the effect of nitrous oxide was short lived, making it unsuitable for long medical operations. Crawford Long, an American physician and pharmacist, was the first to perform surgery using an ether-based anesthetic in 1842.

It was a Scottish gynecologist, James Simpson, who discovered a long-lasting and effective anesthetic in chloroform, in 1847. His aim was to provide pain relief during childbirth. So successful was chloroform as an anesthetic that one mother named her child Anaesthesia. In 1853 Queen Victoria was given chloroform during the birth of her eighth child, Prince Leopold.

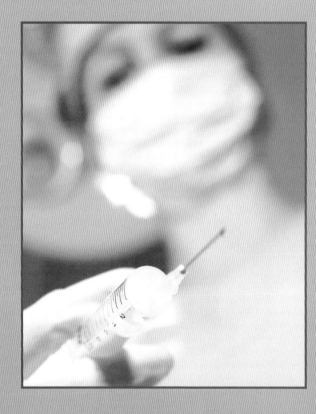

ABOVE James Simpson is found unconscious by his butler having experimented with chloroform. The Scottish gynecologist discovered the anesthetic properties of chloroform in 1847 and soon used them in his practice.

TWO OF THE FIRST PAIN-RELIEVING REMEDIES KNOWN TO BE USED BY THE ANCIENT WORLD WERE MANDRAGORA (MANDRAKE) AND INDIAN HEMP (HASHISH).

THE CLOCK

INVENTOR Unknown   **DATE** Unknown   **COUNTRY** Unknown

ABOVE Christiaan Huyghens, the Dutch physicist who invented the pendulum clock in 1656. His invention greatly impoved the accuracy of time measurement. He also improved teelscope design, and invented a new and more effective way of grinding and polishing lenses.

Devices to tell the time of day, and to predict the seasons, have been in use for thousands of years. The first type of clock to be designed was a sundial, probably in about 3500 BCE, with a pointer casting a shadow across a dial, marked with the hours of the day.

Around 2,000 years later the ancient Egyptians invented more accurate types of clock: the water clock and the hour glass, measuring the constant flow of water or sand from one container to the other. The Chinese developed sophisticated geared mechanisms for telling the time in 200–300 CE, and the Arabs used a celestial planning device called the astrolabe around 400 CE, but the recent discovery of the "Antikythera mechanism" shows that the Greeks had designed sophisticated geared devices to predict movements of the stars in the first century BC.

It is uncertain when exactly the first mechanical clocks were invented and by whom, but due to their growing size, 13th-century religious institutions in Europe needed to tell the time accurately to organize their prayers. Over the following hundred years mechanical clocks became more accurate, chiming the time of day—hence the name "clock," from the French "cloche" or bell.

Various developments over time improved clock accuracy further, including the addition of springs by Peter Heinlein in 1550, Christiaan Huygens' pendulum in 1656, and John Harrison's refinements in the late 1700s. In the early 1800s, mass-production enabled accurate clocks to be reproduced far more cheaply than before, bringing the benefits of accurate timekeeping to the masses. The transmission of Greenwich Mean Time (GMT) in Britain in 1852 ensured that the entire country was working to the same time.

Modern discoveries have also led to great improvements in clock and watch accuracy with atomic, radio-controlled, and quartz timepieces.

"EVEN A STOPPED CLOCK IS RIGHT TWICE A DAY."
MARIE VON EBNER-ESCHENBACH

THE MOST COMMON TYPES OF CLOCK AND WATCH TODAY USE QUARTZ
MECHANISMS. QUARTZ IS A TYPE OF CRYSTAL THAT VIBRATES AT A
VERY CONSTANT RATE WHEN A SMALL ELECTRICAL CURRENT IS PASSED
THROUGH IT, THUS CONTROLLING A CLOCK MOVEMENT VERY PRECISELY.

THE SKYSCRAPER

INVENTOR Le Baron Jenney **DATE** 1884–5 **COUNTRY** USA

ABOVE The Home Insurance Building was built in 1885 in Chicago and demolished in 1931 to make way for the Field Building (now the LaSalle Bank Building). It was the first building to use steel in its frame, though the majority of its structure was composed of cast and wrought iron.

RIGHT The Wainwright Building, built in St. Louis in 1890–1, had a steel frame clad in masonry. Standing ten-stories high, it was used as an office block and was one of the world's earliest skyscrapers.

For the skyscraper to rise, a raft of other developments had to have taken place. These crucial inventions were steel, glass, reinforced concrete, water pumps, and lifts. Until the 19th century there were few buildings of over six storeys. Without elevators, people simply couldn't manage the stairs.

In addition, water pressure was usually insufficient to supply running water above 50 feet (15meters). There were some multi-storey buildings, however. The Romans built eight-storey-high buildings and in Edinburgh, Scotland, the need for more buildings within the limited confines of the city walls led to the construction of 11-storey buildings.

The first skyscraper was the ten-storey Home Insurance Building in Chicago. It was built in 1884–85 by Major William Le Baron Jenney, and used the first load-carrying structural frame. The frame supported the entire weight of the building. Before this, the walls carried the weight of the building. In 1890–1 one of America's finest architects, Louis Henry Sullivan (1856–1924), built The Wainwright Building in St. Louis. The building had a steel frame and for the first time used vertical bands to visually emphasize the height of the building.

"A SKYSCRAPER IS A BOAST IN GLASS AND STEEL."
MASON COOLEY

ORIGINALLY "SKYSCRAPER" WAS A NAUTICAL TERM FOR A TALL MAST ON A SAILING SHIP. IT BEGAN TO BE USED FOR BUILDINGS DURING THE 1880S, SHORTLY AFTER THE FIRST TEN- TO TWENTY-STOREY BUILDINGS WERE BUILT.

FIRE

DISCOVERER Unknown **DATE** Unknown **COUNTRY** Unknown

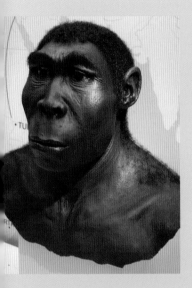

Lightning, natural fires, and volcanic eruptions were most probably man's first experience of fire. Learning how to make fire was the greatest discovery of hominids. It is thought that Homo erectus, a relative of modern humans, may have made fire as early as 790,000 years ago.

ABOVE A depiction of Homo erectus who lived 200,000–1 million years ago. A hominid that used tools, it is thought that Homo erectus would have been able to make fire.

RIGHT This photograph taken in 1914 shows a Koskimo native American using a fire drill. This is a stick that is rotated or rubbed on a base.

Homo erectus would have rubbed together two pieces of wood or two flint stones to produce fire. Later on, fire was produced by striking a piece of iron pyrite with flint stone to produce sparks. Evidence of its use, dating back 10,000–15,000 years, has been found in a Belgian cave.

It has been speculated, however, that the oldest way to make fire would have been to carry a burning coal taken from a natural fire and to keep it smoldering in dry plant material. Many natives in North America still use certain smoldering plants to keep a fire alive for days.

Fire was believed to be the gift of the gods— it gave humankind so much, not least the opportunity to cook meat that was previously eaten raw (thus reducing disease), and to lighten and heat dark caves. The warmth of fire would have been a factor in ensuring man's survival during harsh climates. Fire enabled people to make tools in hot furnaces—axes, knives, saws, hammers, anvils, and weapons made of metal— and its use also allowed the invention of glass.

WITH THE DISCOVERY OF FIRE CAME THE MEANS TO COOK MEAT. SINCE COOKED FOOD IS SOFTER THAN RAW FOOD, THE VERY POWERFUL JAWS OF THE AUSTRALOPITHECINES WERE NOW NO LONGER NEEDED FOR CHEWING.

THE COCKTAIL UMBRELLA

INVENTOR Unknown **DATE** Unknown **COUNTRY** Unknown

Although a seemingly frivolous item, used to decorate drinks or desserts, a cocktail umbrella is actually an ingenious device for preventing a carefully mixed drink from warming above its ideal temperature and, in particular, stops the ice in a cocktail melting.

RIGHT Made from brightly colored printed paper and split bamboo, the cocktail umbrella has come to epitomize the fun and frivolity of the "happy hour."

Made from paper, with cardboard ribs, the miniature umbrella is flexible to fit a range of glass sizes.

The origins of the cocktail umbrella are shrouded in myth and mystery. It is thought that the device was invented in Hawaii, and imported into the USA with returning tourists. However, it is claimed that Don the Beachcomber and Trader Vic's in San Francisco were probably the first bars to use cocktail umbrellas in the USA in the early 1930s. Their association with cocktails and travel to Polynesian islands subsequently meant that the umbrellas became symbols of the exotic and sophisticated, particularly during the 1950s and 1960s.

THE LOCK AND KEY

INVENTOR Unknown **DATE** Unknown **COUNTRY** Unknown

Keeping possessions secure has troubled people since the oldest civilizations. The earliest form of "lock" was probably a sliding bar fixed to the inside of a door that could be engaged to a slot in the door frame, but this was used to keep the door shut rather than restrict access.

This could be reached from the outside of the door by means of a hole and slid into position. An improvement to this basic system was the use of a primitive key to move the bar. However, there is evidence from archeological finds in the Near East that much more complex locks, albeit of wooden construction, were being made as early as 4000 BCE. Ancient Egyptian locks improved on these early designs with arrangements of pins of varying lengths lifted by keys with matching protrusions.

Metal locks, more or less as we know them today, were made by the ancient Romans, together with padlocks, although there is also evidence that these were already in use in China.

Serious improvements in the security of locks were not made until the 18th, 19th, and early 20th centuries. The prolific British inventor Joseph Bramah patented an "unpickable" lock in 1784, relying on precision manufacture—it is still available today. In England, the Chubb company in Wolverhampton made many improvements, as did the Yale company in the USA (founded by Linus Yale, whose family came from North Wales). Linus Yale Junior is credited with the invention of the cylinder lock, for which he was granted patents in the 1860s. These companies are still major players in the lock manufacturing business.

ABOVE An engraving showing the "unpickable" lock patented by Joseph Bramah in 1784.

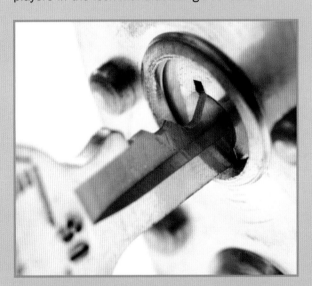

BRAMAH'S "UNPICKABLE" LOCK WAS FINALLY PICKED IN 1851 BY AMERICAN A.C. HOBBS. HE TOOK 16 DAYS TO DO IT.

THE CALCULATOR

INVENTOR Blaise Pascal   **DATE** 1641   **COUNTRY** France

The invention of the handheld calculator changed the daily lives of people throughout the developed world. It meant that basic mathematical problems could be performed more quickly than ever before and with far greater accuracy.

ABOVE The 1970 Canon Pocketronic—the first handheld battery operated calculator.

RIGHT A clerk in 17th century London does his sums with the aid of an adding machine.

The very first counting machine was the abacus (see page 70), invented in Babylonia in around 300 BCE and China in the 2nd century CE. It is questionable as to whether it could be called a calculator, since it was really a memory aid to help a person add up, rather than perform the calculations. The first mechanical calculator to actually do the sum was created in 1641 by a French mathematician, Blaise Pascal. He invented a gear-driven machine that could add and subtract to help his father, a tax collector, in his work. But it was a bank clerk, William Seward Burroughs, who invented the first easily workable adding machine, patented in 1888.

The origin of the modern handheld calculator is also the history of the microchip. Its inventor Jack Kilby had over 60 patents to his credit, but his greatest invention was the monolithic integrated circuit, or microchip, which he developed while leading a team at Texas Instruments. The microchip made microprocessors such as the handheld calculator possible.

The first pocket calculator (the Pocketronic) was invented in 1970–1 and sold 5 million units at $100 a unit. By the mid-1970s, the computing industry was dependent on the microchip, which was and still is used in personal computers, fax machines, cellular phones, and satellite television.

ROLLER SKATES

INVENTOR Monsieur Petibled   **DATE** 1819   **COUNTRY** France

ABOVE From the 1880s, roller skating was a popular pastime in for women in Victorian England. It also gace couritng couples the rare chance to hold hands in public.

RIGHT In the 19th century, roller skating was a popular vaudeville act in the USA. Here, vaudeville star Jesse Darling performs on roller skates with her partner Henry Simmons.

In 1743 roller skates were used in a London stage performance, but there is no record of the inventor's name. In 1760 Jean-Joseph Merlin, a Belgian instrument maker, demonstrated a pair of skates at a London party.

The skates were made from a pair of boots to which several small metal wheels were attached. The story may be apocryphal but it is said that the skates were so uncontrollable that Merlin skated straight into a very large and valuable glass mirror, which he broke. (Merlin, incidentally, was a brilliant inventor, responsible for discoveries and creations in the areas of musical instruments, clocks, and furniture.)

The first patent for roller skates was given to a Monsieur Petitbled in 1819. These early skates could only move in a straight line and consequently were not easy to maneuver. The first quad skates appeared in New York in 1863. Designed by James Leonard Plimpton, they had four wheels set in two pairs and allowed the wearer to turn by leaning to one side. The skates were so successful that the first public skating rink was opened on Rhode Island in 1866. By the 1880s roller skates were being mass-produced in the USA. One manufacturer based in Richmond, Indiana, made thousands of skates a week during one particular peak period of popularity.

The very first roller skates were "inline" skates that used four or five wheels arranged in a line, and were difficult to maneuver. The later quad skates (with wheels arranged in two pairs) were easier to turn and became far more popular and widely used. However, the more difficult inline skates again became popular in the early 1980s and 1990s as a more adventurous and daring form of the sport.

DYNAMITE

INVENTOR Alfred Nobel **DATE** 1867 **COUNTRY** Sweden

The active constituent of dynamite is the explosive liquid chemical, nitroglycerin. It differs from nitroglycerin in that it can be made as a solid and is therefore much more stable.

ABOVE Alfred Nobel, the endower of the Nobel prize, also invented dynamite. His many patents in the area included one for a detonator and another for a blasting gelatine.

RIGHT Women packing dynamite at an explosives factory in Val Bormida, Italy, in 1888.

There had been many accidents in the manufacture, storage, and application of nitroglycerin before the invention of dynamite by Alfred Nobel. Nobel, a Swedish engineer and industrialist born in Stockholm in 1833, was something of a polymath, being well versed in chemistry, philosophy, and languages. In all of these he was self-taught, having no formal university education or degree. He began his industrial career in the construction industry and his interest in explosives was awakened by the need for blasting rocks for building projects. He formed a company in Sweden manufacturing the dangerous and unstable nitroglycerin. Nobel developed dynamite, basically using a buffering agent of silica, to make a much more manageable explosive for which he was granted the patent in 1867.

Subsequent improvements in the formula made it safer still and there was great demand for the product, with factories being opened in Europe, including one in Scotland and one in the USA.

"NOBEL WAS A GENUINE FRIEND OF PEACE. HE EVEN WENT SO FAR AS TO BELIEVE THAT HE HAD INVENTED A TOOL OF DESTRUCTION, DYNAMITE, WHICH WOULD MAKE WAR SO SENSELESS THAT IT WOULD BECOME IMPOSSIBLE. HE WAS WRONG."
ALVA MYRDAL

NOBEL ENDED UP WITH A LARGE INDUSTRIAL EMPIRE, PERSONALLY
HAVING MORE THAN 350 PATENTS TO HIS NAME. UPON HIS DEATH
IN 1896 HE LEFT A LARGE PROPORTION OF HIS FORTUNE TO ENDOW
A FUND TO HONOR THOSE CONSIDERED TO HAVE BENEFITED HUMANITY.

THE MAGNETIC COMPASS

INVENTOR Unknown   **DATE** 11th century   **COUNTRY** China

The magnetic compass was first made in China around the 11th century. Chinese fortune tellers used a mineral called a lodestone in their fortune-telling boards.

Lodestones are composed of an iron oxide, which aligns itself in a north–south direction. When it was found that lodestones could point out true directions, a primitive compass was developed.

The first Chinese compasses were designed on a square slab with markings for the cardinal points and the constellations. The needle was spoon-shaped and made from lodestone, and it had a handle that always pointed south. The introduction of magnetized needles as directional pointers seems to have occurred in the 8th century CE, again in China. When Marco Polo visited China in the 13th century, he brought a compass back to Europe. It was in this same century that the typical magnetic compass as we know it was developed.

Modern handheld navigational compasses use a magnetized needle or dial inside a fluid-filled capsule; the fluid causes the needle to stop quickly rather than oscillate back and forth around magnetic north. The fluid in the capsule is usually oil, kerosene, or alcohol. Pure water cannot be used since it could freeze.

RIGHT The Venetian explorer, Marco Polo, is seen presenting a letter from the Pope to Kublai Khan, the 13th-century Emperor of China. It is during this visit that Marco Polo discovered the Chinese compass and, on his return, he introduced it to Europe.

THE BIKINI

INVENTOR Jacques Heim and Louis Reard   **DATE** 1940s   **COUNTRY** France

Two-piece bathing suits were known in Roman times, but their appearance in the modern world was due to two rival French designers, couturier Jacques Heim and mechanical engineer Louis Reard.

Heim's bikini was the first to be revealed, and he advertised it as "the smallest swimsuit in the world" in skywriting over Cannes in the south of France.

However, his creation was soon overshadowed by an even more revealing suit developed by Louis Reard. It was first modeled at a fashion show on July 5, 1946, four days after the USA had detonated an atomic bomb on Bikini Atoll. Reard named his two-piece "bikini" to reflect his concept of "the ultimate."

The first bikini was modeled by dancer Micheline Bernardi (Reard had been unable to find any models prepared to model the skimpy two-piece). Bernardi's photo was printed around the world, and, although no great beauty, she received around 50,000 fan letters. Reard also hired a skywriter, and introduced the world to "the bikini—smaller than the world's smallest swimsuit."

LEFT Micheline Bernardini modelling Louis Reard's first bikini. The bikini was so small, it was claimed it could fit into the matchbox she is holding.

"A BIKINI IS NOT A BIKINI UNLESS IT CAN BE PULLED THROUGH A WEDDING RING."

LOUIS REARD

The bikini was immediately banned in many Catholic countries and took a number years to find favor in the USA. Its popularity in general, however, was sealed by Bridgit Bardot's bikini-clad appearance in the 1958 hit film *And God Created Women* and Brian Hyland's 1960s song *Itsy Bitsy Teenie Weenie Yellow Polka Dot Bikini*.

SOLAR POWER

INVENTOR Bell Labs   **DATE** 1953   **COUNTRY** USA

The sun emits energy in two forms: heat and light. There are several ancient references to the knowledge that the sun's heat could be concentrated using a magnifying glass or reflection, perhaps the most notable being the story of Archimedes, during the 3rd century BCE, who allegedly used polished bronze mirrors to set fire to Roman ships.

In more recent times, the instances of this principle in action include mirrors to concentrate the sun's rays to produce extreme heat for uses such as de-salination plants in hot countries where water is scarce.

The development of devices to produce electricity directly from light from the sun, however, began in the 19th century when it was discovered that the metal selenium would produce an electric current when exposed to light (known as the photovoltaic or photoelectric effect). The power from this was too feeble to be of much practical use. By the early 20th century, more attention was being paid to the photovoltaic effect of the sun's heat in metal salts like cadmium sulfide. Albert Einstein was among those who wrote papers on the subject and he was awarded a Nobel prize in 1921 for his work describing the photoelectric effect.

The photovoltaic technology used today to produce electricity from sunlight was first developed in 1953, at Bell Labs in New Jersey, when Gerald

Pearson of Bell Labs' semiconductor research group, along with Darryl Chapin and Calvin Fuller, were the first to succeed in producing low-efficiency silicon solar cells, emitting only 2.3 percent of the energy they absorbed. This was still five times better than other methods tried up to that time. Since then, the quest has been to improve efficiency, which is now into double figures. Photovoltaic cells are now used to power a range of devices, and even small villages in hot countries.

RIGHT This 1642 engraving depicts Archimedes using a mirror to concentrate the sun's heat in order to burn the attacking Roman fleet.

ABOVE An array of solar cells in California USA, is used to provide electric power for industrial, commercial, and residential needs.

PLASTIC SURGERY

INVENTOR Unknown   **DATE** 800 BCE   **COUNTRY** India

ABOVE: Cosmetic surgery, that is plastic surgery purely for cosmetic reasons, is now widely accepted. The "tummy tuck", reshaping the eyelids and the facelift are among the most commonly requested procedures.

"Plastic surgery" is defined as a specialized branch of surgery that changes the appearance and function of a person's body. The term was introduced by the German ophthalmologist Carl Ferdinand Von Graefe in 1818, plastic being derived from the Greek word "plastikos," meaning to reshape or to mold.

Plastic surgery originated in ancient India where, as early as 800 BCE, skin grafts were used to reconstruct facial features. The principles of the surgery are set down by Sushruta in *c*.600 BCE in his work *Sushruta Samhita*, which describes a number of procedures such as the reconstruction of ears (otoplasty) and noses (rhinoplasty).

In Europe, the Romans were able to undertake simple procedures from about the 1st century BCE. Plastic surgery did not develop further until the 19th and 20th centuries, however, when general surgical procedures such as anesthetics and disinfection, as well as an understanding of the importance of a sterile environment, became commonplace.

In 1918, Dr Harold Delf Gillies became the first modern physician to specialize in plastic surgery. Born in New Zealand, he studied and worked in England, and is regarded as the father of modern plastic surgery through his pioneering work helping victims of facial injury from World War I. During World War II, one of Gillies' students, Archibald McIndoe, developed his techniques further while treating badly burned airmen at a hospital in West Sussex, England, which became known as the "Guinea Pig Club."

Today, many plastic surgeons also perform cosmetic surgery, such as "face lifts," that are unrelated to medical conditions and are undertaken solely to improve appearance.

"OFTEN WHILE LIFTING A FACE I HAVE A FEELING OF GUILT THAT I AM MERELY MAKING MONEY, YET, IS IT NOT JUSTIFIED IF IT BRINGS EVEN A LITTLE EXTRA HAPPINESS TO A SOUL WHO NEEDS IT?"
DR HAROLD DELF GILLIES

THE LIGHT BULB

INVENTOR Thomas Edison   **DATE** 1879   **COUNTRY** USA

The invention of the light bulb proved to be a spark of brilliance that radically changed people's lives for the simple reason that they were now able to pursue a whole range of work and leisure activities after dusk that would have previously been denied them.

Thomas Edison developed a practical light bulb toward the end of 1879. His was not the first light bulb to be invented but it was the first one to be commercially viable. For the light bulb to be of real practical use, it had to last a long time, so creating a successful filament that possessed high electrical resistance was essential. By 1879, Edison had produced a high resistance lamp in a very high vacuum, which would burn for 1,500 hours. In 1880 he designed a version that demonstrated all the essential features of a modern light bulb: an incandescent filament (which glowed when an electric current was passed through it) in an evacuated glass bulb with a screw base.

The first public demonstration of Thomas Edison's incandescent lighting system was in December, 1879, when he electrically lit the Menlo Park laboratory complex in New Jersey. Edison spent the next several years developing the electric industry (see page 14).

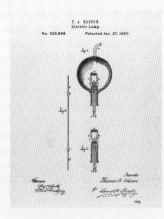

ABOVE: Patent No: 223, 898 for Edison's lightbulb, dated January 27, 1880. The patent for his incandescent lightbulb ushered in the age of domestic lighting. It is one of over a thousand patents to emerge from Edison's laboratory in New Jersey, USA.

"GENIUS IS ONE PERCENT INSPIRATION AND NINETY-NINE PERCENT PERSPIRATION."
THOMAS EDISON

THE ROLLER COASTER

INVENTOR LaMarcus Thompson **DATE** 1884 **COUNTRY** USA

ABOVE: This newspaper illustration shows daytrippers enjoying an early roller coaster ride at Coney Island, USA, in 1886.

The world's very first roller coaster-type rides were the Russian Ice Slides. These slides first appeared during the 17th century throughout Russia. Built out of wood to heights of 70–80 feet (23–26.5 meters), they were covered with a sheet of ice several inches thick.

By the late 1700s, their popularity was such that designers attempted to copy the idea using wheeled cars on tracks. By the 1880s inventors were experimenting with the vertical loop.

In the USA, in 1873, "gravity rail road" was introduced. It was called the Mauch Chunk Switchback Railroad and was created by a mining company in the mountains of Pennsylvania. An old coal train was pushed up the hill by a coal engine and then allowed to "runaway" down to the base of the hill.

The first modern roller coaster designer was LaMarcus Thompson. He created a roller coaster in Coney Island in 1884 and patented his "Roller Coasting Structure" in 1885. However, the person who is thought of as the "Thomas Edison of the roller coaster" is John A. Miller (real name August John Mueller), who successfully registered more than 100 patents related to coaster rides.

Miller's inventions included many of the safety features that are still found in today's roller coasters. These include his 1919 invention of "underfriction wheels." It is this technology that keeps the coaster cars locked to their tracks, thus allowing the cars to reach high speeds, turn at sharp angles, as well as upside down.

Miller designed roller coasters for amusement parks all over the world, including the Cyclone at Puritas Springs in Cleveland, Ohio (which appears on the Smithsonian Institution's list of Great Lost Roller Coasters), and the Big Dipper at Blackpool Pleasure Beach in the UK. Today a few of his roller coasters remain in operation, including The Racer Coaster at Kennywood Park, near Pittsburgh, Pennsylvania.

THE BICYCLE

INVENTOR Ernest Michaux   **DATE** 1861   **COUNTRY** France

ABOVE: Baron von Drais' 1816 bicycle illustrated in the UK *Mechanics' Magazine*, 1832.

Although Leonardo da Vinci drew some rough sketches of a contraption that resembled a bicycle, Count Mede de Sivrac of France is usually credited as the designer of the first bicycle in 1790.

Referred to as a hobbyhorse or celeripede, it was made of wood and the rider had to use his feet to propel it forward, since it had no pedals. In 1816, Baron Karl von Drais de Sauerbrun of Germany invented a model with a steering bar attached to the front wheel, which he called a "Draisienne." This model had two wheels, between which the rider sat. However, there were still no pedals. These were added in 1840 by a Scottish blacksmith, Kirkpatrick Macmillan, who is credited with inventing the true bicycle. In 1861 the first modern bicycle with pedals and cranks was invented by Ernest Michaux. By 1865 the Michaux family were producing 4,000 bicycles a year.

In 1871 the Penny Farthing was invented by a British engineer, James Starley. It proved to be the first really efficient bicycle. It consisted of a small rear wheel and large front wheel pivoting on a simple tubular frame with tires of rubber.

RIGHT: An 1887 illustration showing a cycling party. The women ride three-wheelers and the men higher two-wheelers.

"DISCOVERED FEWER THAN 20 YEARS AGO, IT HAS ADDED A NEW PLEASURE TO LIFE, OPENED A NEW AVENUE TO HEALTH FOR COUNTLESS THOUSANDS OF ALL AGES AND BOTH SEXES, AND—WHICH IS VERY WELL WORTH NOTING—CREATED A NEW AND IMPORTANT BUSINESS INTEREST OF VAST AND STILL GROWING DIMENSION."
THE BOOM IN BICYCLING, *THE BOSTON GLOBE* JULY 27, 1891

A CYCLIST CAN MOVE THREE OR FOUR TIMES FASTER THAN A PEDESTRIAN, BUT USES FIVE TIMES LESS ENERGY IN THE PROCESS.

THE HAMMOCK

INVENTOR Mayan Indians   **DATE** 1000 CE   **COUNTRY** Yucatán, Central America

The hammock is a woven net-like bed, hung above the ground from two points, one at either end. It is believed that it was first used by Mayan Indians in the Yucatán region of Central America about 1,000 years ago, and the hammock forms an important part of the culture of the Yucatán people to this day.

Originally woven from fibers from the bark of the Hamak tree, and later made from sisal fibers, hammocks were traded and adopted by other civilizations throughout Central and South America. The English word "hammock" probably comes from the Spanish word "hamaca," which was in turn taken from the Haitian word meaning "fish net."

Hammocks were taken back to Europe in the 15th century by the explorer Christopher Columbus, and were very quickly adopted by European navies as convenient, compact, and collapsible beds for their sailors, made from the canvas of old sails. They had the added advantage of raising their occupants off the deck or ground, away from dirt, vermin, and disease.

Today, hammocks are made in a wide range of designs and materials, including cotton and special moisture- and mosquito-resistant fabrics.

THE TYPEWRITER

INVENTOR Christopher Latham Sholes **DATE** 1867 **COUNTRY** USA

The first-ever typewriter was invented by an Englishman, Henry Mills, in 1714, for which Queen Anne granted him a patent. An American surveyor, William Austin Burt, invented a writing machine he called the Typographer in 1829 but, due to lack of financial backing, it never went into mass production.

ABOVE: A Victorian women uses Sholes's typewriter. This typewriter had the Qwerty keyboard layout that English-language computer keyboards still use today.

Two Americans, Christopher Latham Sholes and Samuel W. Soule, succeeded in making a practical model in 1867 and patented it in 1868. Sholes' first typewriter machine was made with part of an old table, a circular piece of glass, a telegraph key, a piece of carbon paper, and piano wire. By 1909 typewriters were in mass production and were being sold in the USA, France, Germany, England, Switzerland, and Japan.

The initial public reaction to typewritten letters was anger. People thought them impersonal and saw them also as a comment on their inability to read handwriting. It was only when the idea of "scientific management" (the specialization of work, with some people, for example, doing correspondence and others accounts) became popular that the typewriter came into its own. And, as enterprises got bigger and the Industrial Revolution speeded up trade and commerce, the old-fashioned idea of the handwritten business letter was simply impossible.

IN 1874 MARK TWAIN SAW A WOMAN IN A SHOP WINDOW DEMONSTRATING A NEW INVENTION CALLED THE "TYPE-WRITER." SHE WAS ABLE TO TYPE OVER FIFTY WORDS PER MINUTE.

THE GLOBAL POSITIONING

INVENTOR US Department of Defense   **DATE** 1970s   **COUNTRY** USA

ABOVE: A waterproof GPS device for use by hikers and sailors.

The global positioning system, universally referred to as GPS, was developed by the US Department of Defense, its official title being: Navstar GPS (NAVigation Satellite Timing And Ranging Global Positioning System). Its purpose was originally military, but it was also offered free for civilian use.

The entire system consists of a network of at least 24 satellites, orbiting at a height of 20,200 kilometers (12,552 miles), transmitting signals so that a receiver on the ground can establish its accurate position by measuring the distance between itself and three or more satellites.

The GPS receiver has an antenna tuned to the frequency transmitted by the satellites, a processor, and a quartz clock, and usually a display screen, or "moving map," most useful for cars, boats, and aircraft, to show the position. The system is still prone to interference from thunderstorms, bursts of solar radiation, or man-made electromagnetic signals.

There has been a huge increase in sales of GPS devices to motorists, walkers, mountaineers, and sailors. There are many uses: GPS is now considered an essential tool for marine navigation, and aircraft are routinely fitted with the system. Agricultural machinery can be automatically steered by satellite signal. There are also applications in earth-moving and open-cast mining machinery. Also, users of mobile telephones can be accurately located, which can be useful for the emergency services.

LEFT: An artist's impression of the Navstar-2F satellite of the Global Positioning System in orbit.

SYSTEM

THE COST OF OPERATING THE GPS IS ESTIMATED AT ROUGHLY $750 MILLION PER YEAR.

THE RADIO

INVENTOR Guglielmo Marconi   **DATE** 1901   **COUNTRY** Italy

The invention of radio grew out of many inventions and discoveries that preceded it. It depended in part on Michael Faraday's demonstration that an electrical current could produce a magnetic field.

The theory of radio transmission, or "telegraphy without wires," was first put forward by British physicist James Clerk Maxwell in 1864. He argued that radio waves behaved as light does, and traveled at the speed of light. In 1888 Heinrich Hertz in Germany demonstrated that Maxwell's theory was correct. However, it was a young Italian physicist, Guglielmo Marconi, who realized the potential of radio for communication. In 1901 he produced a radio system that transmitted Morse code over the Atlantic Ocean. In 1903 Marconi

demonstrated that radio waves could cross the Atlantic. In 1906 an American physicist, Lee De Forest, invented the vacuum tube which amplified radio signals that were received by antenna. This meant that much weaker signals could be transmitted over longer distance. The vacuum tube was also used to generate radio waves and soon become the main component of radio transmitter. Further developments by other scientists made speech and music broadcasts possible.

In the USA there was no government restriction on use of the airwaves and hundreds of radio stations soon sprang up. In Britain, the government allowed the Marconi Company to broadcast only one evening a week.

TOP LEFT: Guglielmo Marconi (1874–1937) was responsible for the invention of the radio. In 1909 he won the Nobel Prize for Physics. As a boy he had experimented with electrical circuits and, in 1895, he succeeded in sending wireless signals over a distance of one and a half miles (2.5 kilometers).

BELOW Radio broadcasts became very important during World War II. Here, Franklin Roosevelt is pictured giving a wartime radio address.

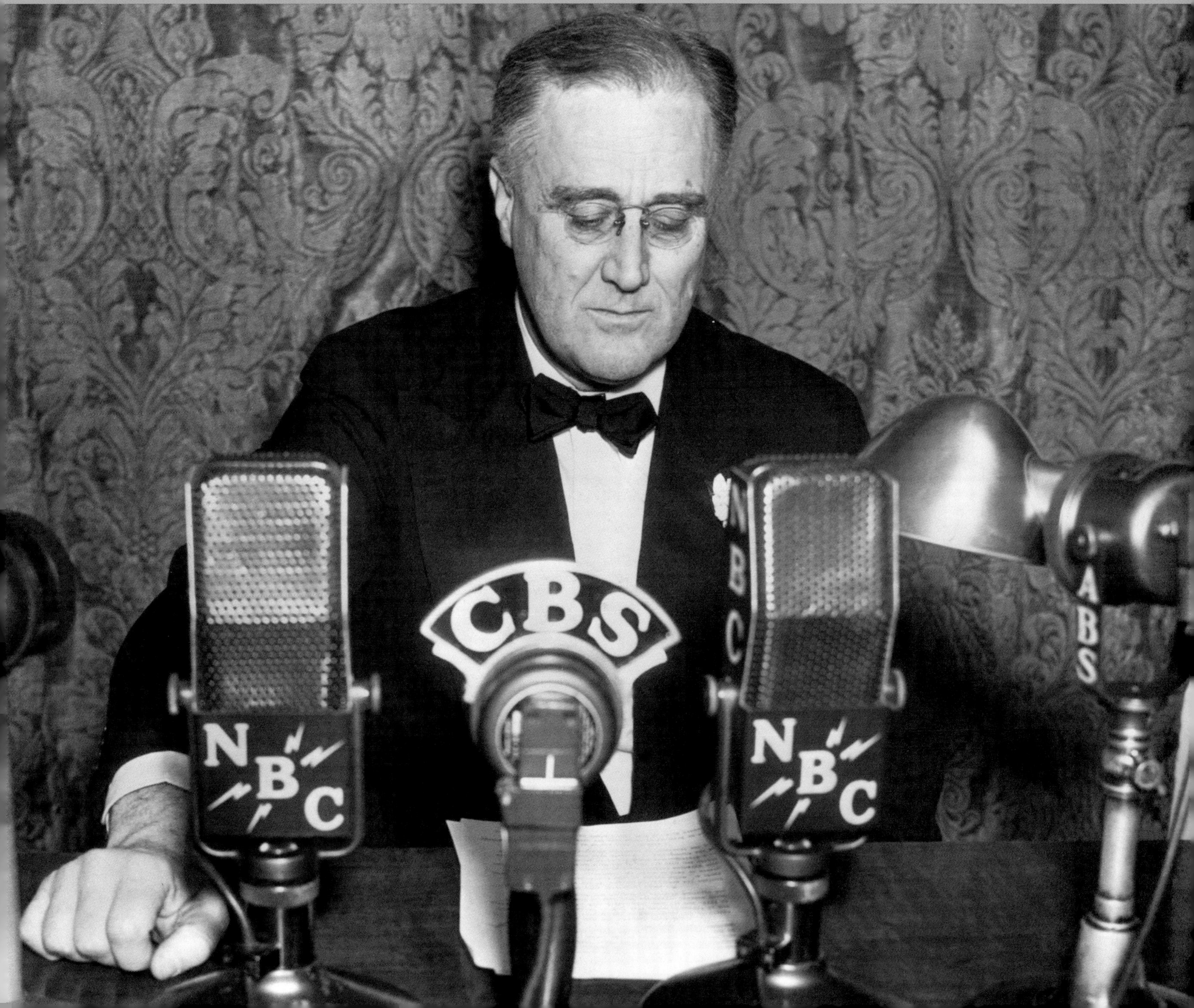

THE TEA BAG

INVENTOR Thomas Sullivan   **DATE** 1908   **COUNTRY** USA

Tea has existed as a beverage since 2737 BCE in China. An unknown Chinese inventor invented the tea shredder, a small device that shredded tea leaves in preparation for drinking. For many centuries, the length of time the tea was left in the pot has been considered of importance to the quality of the brew.

RIGHT: The first four-sided tea bag was designed by Thomas Lipton in 1952. He called it the "flo-thru" tea bag, and it allowed the tea to seep through more quickly than two-sided bags.

Various methods of allowing tea to be easily removed from the pot, such as metal infusers, were developed. In around 1908, Thomas Sullivan, a New-York tea merchant, started to send samples of tea to his customers in small silken bags. His customers thought the bags were meant to be used in the same way as the metal infusers and so dropped them into the pot. Because the fine mesh of the silk material didn't allow the tea to infuse, Sullivan received complaints. Realizing the importance of his accidental invention, he developed sachets made of gauze.

By the 1920s tea bags were being commercially manufactured in the USA, and the gauze material was replaced with thin paper. The tea bag, as we know it, was born.

"WOULDN'T IT BE DREADFUL TO LIVE IN A COUNTRY WHERE THEY DIDN'T HAVE TEA."
NÖEL COWARD

THE FIRE EXTINGUISHER

INVENTOR Captain George Manby   **DATE** 1819   **COUNTRY** UK

It is known that Ctesibius of Alexandria invented a hand pump able to deliver water to a fire in about 200 BCE, and the ancient Romans used buckets passed from one person to another to deliver water to a fire. A "squirt," or hand water pump, was developed in the Middle Ages to douse fires and these continued in use for several hundred years.

The earliest patent of a device to extinguish fires was granted to Nicolaas and John van der Heyden in Holland in 1677; other patents were filed by France C. Hoffer in 1722, Alanson Crane in 1863, and Thomas Martin (an African American) in 1872. However, the first portable fire extinguisher that resembles the modern device was invented in England by Captain George Manby in 1819. It consisted of a copper vessel containing a fire-repressing potassium carbonate solution that squirted onto a fire using compressed air.

Nowadays the portable extinguisher will always take the form of a cylinder with some sort of trigger or lever at the top to release the contents onto the fire. There are several types, filled with different extinguishing agents, suitable for different types of fire. For example, water, being a good conductor of electricity, should clearly not be used where electricity is involved.

Fire extinguishers are universally sited in public buildings, offices, schools, etcetera, where they are a safety and an insurance requirement.

Where national jurisdiction demands they are compulsory in public transport, road haulage, and other such potential risk areas.

ABOVE: Tackling a small fire with a fire extinguisher can make the difference between a small incident and a full-scale disaster.

IN EUROPE, THE BODIES OF FIRE EXTINGUISHERS ARE PAINTED AND COLOR-CODED TO SIGNIFY THEIR SUITABILITY FOR VARIOUS TYPES OF CONFLAGRATION, AND THESE COLORS ARE GOVERNED BY EUROPEAN STANDARDS. THE USA USES A SYSTEM OF PICTOGRAMS.

CHESS

INVENTOR Unknown **DATE** Unknown **COUNTRY** India

Chess is a competitive and recreational game played between two players on a checkered board with 64 squares, alternately black and white. Both players, start the game with 16 black or white pieces; each piece can be moved only according to its own particular restrictions.

RIGHT: A Saracen and an Arab are depicted playing chess in this 13th century manuscript. The manuscript was written by Alfonso The Wise, a 13th-century Spanish king. The Arab conquest of Spain spread the game to Europe in the 10th century.

"CHESS IS THE GYMNASIUM OF THE MIND."
ADOLF ANDERSSEN

The object of the game is to force your opponent into such a position that he or she would be unable to move without the loss of their "king" piece. This position is called "checkmate." Games may also be drawn if a "stalemate" is reached, where no one can move to any effect. In serious competition chess, moves may be "timed out" if a player takes longer to make a move than the stipulated time limit.

Chess is an ancient game. How ancient or precisely where it originated is a matter of conjecture. It is believed to have come originally from India, but it is known that it was also played in China and Arabia. One clue is that an Indian game similar to chess exists called "chaturanga," which appears to resemble closely a game recorded from Persia in the 6th century as "shatranj." Another theory is that the game originated in China.

The Arabs acquired the game during their invasions of Persia, and then brought it to Europe when they conquered Spain in the 10th century. The chess pieces used in the "modern" game date from the Middle Ages and so represent figures familiar at that time—bishops, castles (otherwise known as rooks), knights, pawns (representing serfs), and a king and queen.

A COMPUTER (OR, RATHER, ITS PROGRAMMER) BEAT A CHESS
GRAND MASTER FOR THE FIRST TIME WHEN AN IBM MACHINE
BEAT GARY KASPOROV, THEN WORLD CHAMPION, IN 1997.

THE STEAM ENGINE

INVENTOR Thomas Savery   **DATE** 18th century   **COUNTRY** UK

Although the Scotsman James Watt has often been credited with inventing the steam engine, the potential power of steam had been recognized since ancient times. For example, in the 2nd century BCE, Hero of Alexandria wrote about using steam to power a machine that would open the temple doors.

ABOVE: James Watt (1736–1819) charged his customers a premium for using his steam engines, comparing the power of the engine to that of a horse. He calculated that a horse exerted a pull of 180 pounds (82 kilograms), and described his machine as having "a 20 horse-power engine."

RIGHT: The prototype for James Watt's steam engine "Old Bess" built in 1777.

Whether he actually made this invention is unrecorded. The first known steam engine used steam, which expands when heated in a boiler, to raise a piston up and down in a cylinder. It was invented in the UK in the 1700s by Thomas Savery. He used his engine to pump water out of mines, and called it "The Miner's Friend." However, it was James Watt (the unit of power, the "watt," was named after him) who saw the potential of steam to drive factory machinery. The first of Watt's engines appeared in 1777.

The invention of the steam engine powered the Industrial Revolution. Since the energy it provided was not dependent on water power, factories could be located anywhere. In 1885 the English engineer George Stephenson developed his first locomotion engine, calling it "The Rocket." The speed of steam locomotives and steamships revolutionized trade and industry, and by the early 1900s, express steam locomotives had begun to appear.

IN THE LATE 19TH CENTURY A CERTAIN RUFUS PORTER, FOUNDER OF *SCIENTIFIC AMERICAN*, PLANNED TO FLY PASSENGERS ON PROPELLER-DRIVEN BALLOONS POWERED BY STEAM ENGINES. RATHER LUCKILY, HIS "AIRLINE" NEVER TOOK OFF.

THE ZIPPER

INVENTOR Whitcomb L. Judson   **DATE** 1893   **COUNTRY** USA

ABOVE: By the late 1920s, zippers could be found in all kinds of clothing, footwear, and leather goods.

THE INDUSTRIALIST B.F. GOODRICH COINED THE ONOMATOPOEIC TERM "ZIPPER" IN 1923.

Before the zipper was invented boots could only be laced, which was a slow process. To get around this, inventor Whitcomb L. Judson created two thin metal chains that could be fastened together by pulling a slider up between them. He patented this "clasp locker or unlocker for shoes" in 1891.

He then formed the Automatic Hook and Eye Company with a friend, Colonel Lewis Walker. The two men soon realized that their hookless fastener could be used to replace all buttons, eyes, and hooks on clothes and shoes. In 1896 they developed the Universal Fastener. Judson then developed a simplified fastener, the C-Curity, which sold for 35 cents in 1910, for use on men's trouser flies and women's skirts. The zipper really came into its own when Gideon Sunback, a Westinghouse engineer, joined Judson and Walker. By 1913, Sunback had invented an improved "separable fastener," offering more versatility. The American military ordered them in vast quantities.

Today, thousands of zipper miles are produced daily and the various types available include invisible, metallic, and plastic zippers.

VACCINATION

INVENTOR Edaward Jenner **DATE** 1798 **COUNTRY** UK

The word "vaccination" comes from the Latin "vacca," meaning "cow." It was so called because the first vaccine was derived from a virus affecting cows (the cowpox virus), which was found to provide some immunity to smallpox.

This discovery was made in 1798 by an English country doctor called Edward Jenner. He had always been fascinated by the old wives' tale that milkmaids could not get smallpox, although they often suffered from cowpox, a lesser, non-threatening virus. He speculated that the pus in the cowpox blisters somehow protected the milkmaids.

Jenner took the unusual step of experimenting on a young boy. He took some pus from cowpox blisters found on the hand of a milkmaid and "injected" it into the young boy. He built up the doses over several days and then deliberately injected him with smallpox. Luckily for Jenner, the boy soon recovered completely after a short illness. So successful was Jenner's discovery that in 1840 the government of the day banned any alternative treatments for smallpox.

Jenner's work paved the way for other scientists to develop new vaccines following the same principle. In 1885 Louis Pasteur developed a vaccine against rabies, and in 1955 Jonas Salk developed a vaccination against polio.

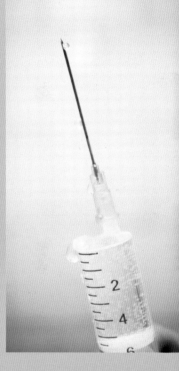

LEFT: This 1802 cartoon by James Gillray captures the public and government's inital opposition to vaccination. Entitled "The cow pock or the wonderful effect of the new innoculation", it show cows emerging from vaccinated people. After initial scepticism, however, most doctors were using the vaccination by 1800.

^{THE}WORLD WIDE WEB

INVENTOR Tim Berners-Lee **DATE** 1980s **COUNTRY** UK

In 1958 America's Defense Department, the Pentagon, created a new research body called the Advanced Research Projects Agency (ARPA) in response to the Soviet Union's launching of Sputnik, the first satellite in space.

An important ARPA research project was designing and developing a command and control network for the US military that would survive a nuclear attack. During the 1960s, this research resulted in advances in data transfer over wired networks and the setting up of a system called the ARPANET, where computers were connected together to enable the exchange of data. On January 1, 1983, the US National Science Foundation (NSF) set up the first network connecting computers at different sites—or internet—using a communication language known as Transmission Control Protocol/Internet Protocol, or TCP/IP—the standard that all internet networks use today.

By the late 1980s, this computer network had expanded internationally to encompass commercial "gateways" to the network as well as the educational research community. Two scientists, Tim Berners-Lee from Britain and Robert Caillieu from Belgium, working for CERN (the European particle research laboratory in Geneva, Switzerland), devised a system for viewing and sharing files more easily using "hypertext," creating what they called a "world wide web." By

the 1990s, Berners-Lee's work made the first hypertext files available for "downloading."

Since then, the ever-expanding internet has been serviced by commercial Internet Service Providers (ISPs), companies that provide connection to the internet for fees from users. Until recently, "dial-up" connection had been slow and expensive but this is now being remedied by the "broadband" connection, which transfers data at a much faster rate and has fueled the increase in "on-line" shopping, including the downloading of music and video through the internet.

RIGHT: The workstation used by Tim Berners-Lee and Robert Caillieu for the first Web server on the World Wide Web.

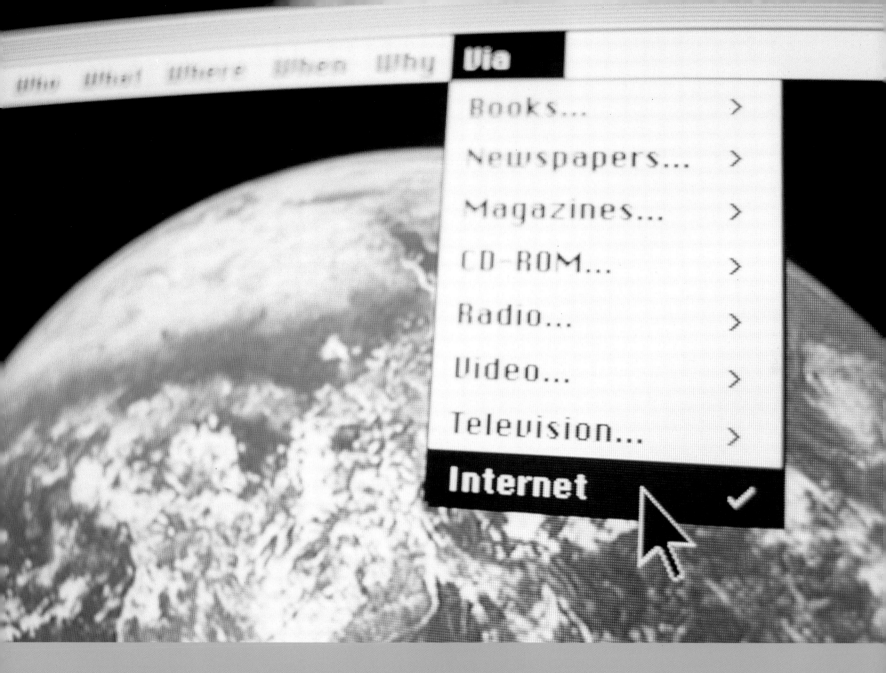

**"ON THE INTERNET, NOBODY
KNOWS YOU'RE A DOG."**
PETER STEINER, *THE NEW YORKER*, JULY 1993

PLUMBING

INVENTOR Unknown   **DATE** Unknown   **COUNTRY** Ancient Rome

Plumbing comes from the Latin word "plumbum" meaning "lead." Basic forms of plumbing have existed for centuries. For example, over 2,800 years ago, King Minos of Crete had the first known flushing toilet, and a toilet was discovered in the tomb of a Chinese king of the Western Han Dynasty dating back to between 206 BCE–24 CE.

Some historians trace the development of plumbing in the Western world to Mesopotamia, where earthenware pipes, masonry sewers, and toilets were in use as early as 2500 BCE. It was the ancient Romans, however, who really developed the idea of plumbing. They created systems of sewers and built outhouses or latrines directly over the running waters of the sewers.

In Europe in the Middle Ages chamber pots were used. They consisted of a metal or ceramic bowl, the contents being thrown out of the window. This was highly unsanitary and many commentators of the time felt that there must be a better way of removing human waste. In 1596, a flush toilet was invented and built for Queen Elizabeth I by her godson, Sir John Harrington. The first patent for the flushing toilet was issued to Alexander Cummings in 1775, not to Thomas Crapper, as is often assumed. It was, however, the cholera epidemic in London between 1844 and 1855 that led to the need for a new sewerage system and the true appearance of the flush toilet.

Sprinto non spinto.   More feard than hurt.

ABOVE: Illustration from Sir John Harrington's book *The Metamorphosis of Ajax*. Harrington installed a water closet in his house in 1596.

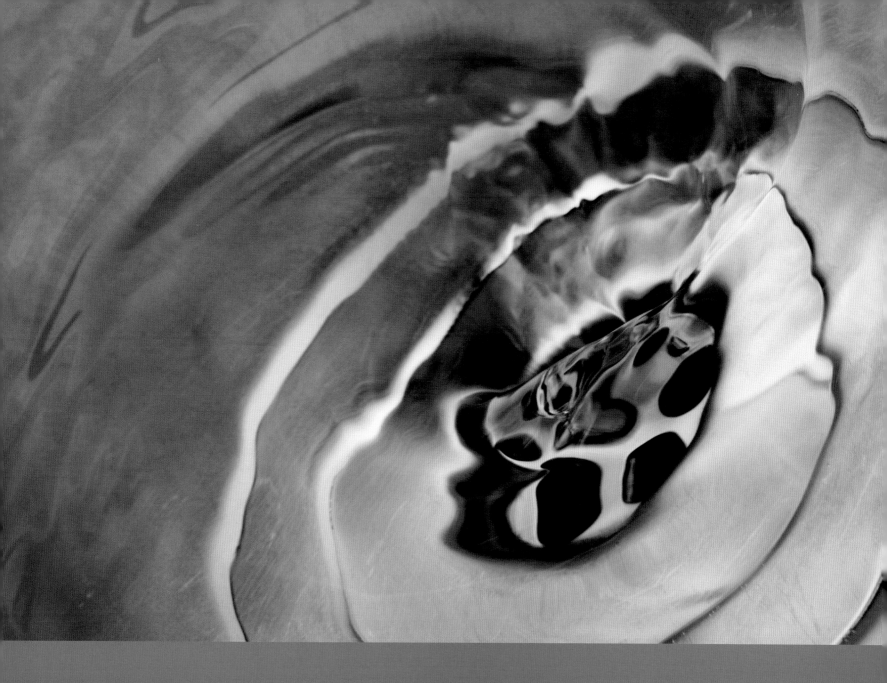

ALBERT EINSTEIN WAS NAMED AN HONORARY MEMBER
OF THE US PLUMBERS AND STEAMFITTERS UNION AFTER
PUBLICLY STATING THAT IF HE WERE TO LIVE HIS LIFE
AGAIN HE WOULD BECOME A PLUMBER.

THE REFRIGERATOR

INVENTOR Carl von Linde   **DATE** 1876   **COUNTRY** Germany

Since prehistoric times, people have preserved food by keeping it cool, and the very first "refrigerators" were caves packed with ice or snow. Later on, the Greeks and Romans placed large amounts of snow into storage pits dug into the ground, and insulated them with wood and straw.

RIGHT: Today's fridges are a design item as well as a necessary kitchen appliance.

The first practical refrigerating machine, built by Jacob Perkins in 1834, used ether in a vapor compression cycle. An American doctor, John Gorrie, built a refrigerator in 1844 to make ice to cool the air for his yellow fever patients. However, the refrigerator as we know it was created by a German engineer, Carl von Linden, who patented not a refrigerator but the process of liquifying gas in 1877.

The refrigerator works by removing heat from an enclosed space, or from a substance, to lower its temperature. It does this by using the evaporation of a liquid to absorb heat. The liquid used in a refrigerator evaporates at an extremely low temperature, creating freezing temperatures inside the unit.

Surprisingly, mass production of refrigerators didn't start until after World War II.

THE YO-YO

INVENTOR Unknown **DATE** Unknown **COUNTRY** Unknown

The ubiquitous child's toy, the yo-yo, consists of a short central spindle joining two narrow flanges, with a cord loosely attached to the spindle. The cord is looped over a finger and then wound around the spindle so that the yo-yo can be held in the hand. When released down the cord, it spins rapidly.

At the limit of travel, by virtue of its kinetic energy, the yo-yo then winds itself back up the cord toward the hand.

The yo-yo is an ancient toy, with examples found in Greece dating from 500 BCE, but the name itself is said to be of Filipino origin. There was said to be a weapon of this name consisting of a disc with sharp, serrated edges, spun by a rope, although this seems unlikely to have been very effective.

A craze for the yo-yo has at various times swept through Europe and the USA. A patent was granted in 1866 to James Haven for the toy, then called a "whirligig." It did not really catch on until 1928, when Pedro Flores, a Filipino-American, started the Yo-Yo Manufacturing Company in California. About two years later the company was bought by Donald Duncan who eventually sold it to Flambeau Plastics who still make yo-yos today.

LEFT: One of the world's oldest toys, the word "yo-yo" is said to come from the Tagalog language (the language of the Philippines), meaning "to come back."

A "WORLD" YO-YO CONTEST IS HELD EVERY YEAR IN FLORIDA, WHERE COMPULSORY TRICKS AND FREESTYLE PERFORMANCES ARE JUDGED.

THE NEON LIGHT

INVENTOR Georges Claude **DATE** 1910 **COUNTRY** France

In 1675 French astronomer Jean Picard discovered that the mercury in a barometer emitted a faint glow. When the barometer was shaken he observed that the strength of the glow increased.

ABOVE: Before the 1930s neon lighting was restricted to red or blue. In the 1934, Erich Koch, a German inventor, created a method of applying a fluorescent powder coating on the inner surface of glass tubes. By exposing the tubes to ultraviolet radiation he produced a variety of colors.

RIGHT: Georges Claude in his laboratory. An engineer and chemist, he invented the neon light, which was the forerunner of the fluorescent light.

Although Picard and other scientists were interested in this concept, it would take the invention of electricity for barometric light to be understood. In 1910 a French inventor Georges Claude demonstrated how he could apply an electrical charge to a sealed tube of neon gas to create a lamp. He created a company to manufacture his invention. He sold two neon lights to the car manufacturer Packard in the USA. Each sign displayed the name "Packard" and was sold for $12,000 in 1923. Their visibility, by day as well as by night meant that neon light soon became a very popular form of outdoor advertising.

Inside the glass tube of a neon light there is a gas such as neon, argon, or krypton at low pressure. At both ends of the tube there are metal electrodes. When a high voltage is applied to the electrodes, the neon gas ionizes, and electrons flow through the gas. The gas molecules travel in all directions, colliding with one another constantly. Each collision causes the molecules involved to emit light.

NEON NATURALLY PRODUCES A RED GLOW. THE OTHER
COLORS IN NEON LIGHTS ARE MADE BY ADDING DIFFERENT
GASES SUCH AS ARGON, MERCURY, AND PHOSPHOR.

BUNGEE JUMP

INVENTOR Unknown   **DATE** Unknown   **COUNTRY** Unknown

Bungee jumping is a "dangerous sport" which consists of jumping from a high point, such as a bridge or crane, whilst attached to a strong elastic cord, and bouncing several times after the cord has stretched to its full length. The attraction of bungee jumping is found in the thrill of the adrenaline rush and conquering the fear of falling from a great height.

RIGHT: Land divers jump from a 100 foot (30 meter) tower in Vanuatu, on Pentecost Island in the South Pacific. An ancient tradition on the island, it was originally practiced to encourage a good yam crop. It is still a powerful and popular ritual today.

The origins of bungee jumping can be traced to the ancient ritual of land diving found on Pentecost Island, Vanuatu, in the South Pacific. Young men jump from a specially constructed bamboo tower about 100 feet (30 meters) high, attached by their feet to the top of the tower using specially selected vines. This rite of passage was recorded for television in the 1950s by David Attenborough and a BBC film crew; it is thought that this film inspired Chris Baker from Bristol, England, to use specially made elastic ropes to undertake similar jumps.

The first bungee jump in England was made by four members of the Oxford University's Dangerous Sports Club from Clifton Suspension Bridge in Bristol on 1 April 1979. They were immediately arrested for undertaking the high-risk leaps, but persevered with further highly publicized jumps around the world. The first commercial bungee-jumping activities were run by A.J. Hackett in Auckland, New Zealand. Today, bungee jumping continues around the world as a carefully supervised sport, with jumpers being attached to the elastic rope using specially made feet and body harnesses.

THE BIGGEST RECORDED BUNGEE JUMP WAS MADE BY JOCHEN
SCHWIZER IN GERMANY ON SEPTEMBER 19, 1997. HE JUMPED
1,246 FEET (380 METERS) USING A 931-FOOT (284-METER)
CORD SUSPENDED FROM A HOVERING HELICOPTER.

THE PRODUCTION LINE

INVENTOR Unknown **DATE** 16th century **COUNTRY** Italy

A production line is a sequence of operations where components are assembled to produce an end-product or where raw materials, such as metal ores or agricultural products, are put through a number of processes to produce a finished article.

ABOVE *C.*1913, factory workers assemble a Model T automobile at the Ford factory in Michegan, USA.

Although the production line is considered a product of the Industrial Revolution, the oldest-known production line was constructed in the Venice Arsenal in the 16th century. This shipyard and naval depot was mass-producing ships using components and assembly lines. By the early 16th century, at the peak of its operation, the Arsenal employed 16,000 people and was able to manufacture nearly one ship per day. The production line was not seen again until the late 18th century.

Early attempts to engineer production processes were hampered by the lack of an energy source. This was solved by the invention of the steam engine in the second half of the 18th century, which enabled the production processes to be brought into one building. In the 1780s, Oliver Evans in the USA is credited as developing the first production line, where he brought together the various stages of the flour- milling process.

The principle of the production line was made popular by Henry Ford. In 1913 he introduced the concept of continuously moving the Model T cars past individual workstations for assembly.

The production line has served to reduce human error and labor costs, and, delivered increased rates of productivity. Improvements to the production line have included greater automation and the use of computer-controlled robots to perform many functions. However, once put in place, a production line can be difficult to change.

FORD'S ASSEMBLY LINE IN MICHIGAN PRODUCED ONE MODEL T CAR
EVERY 93 MINUTES AND, BY 1914, THE SYSTEM WAS DELIVERING
700,000 CARS PER YEAR—TWICE THE PRODUCTION OF ALL THE OTHER
CONTEMPORARY MANUFACTURERS COMBINED.

THE FOUNTAIN PEN

INVENTOR Unknown   **DATE** 17th century   **COUNTRY** France

ABOVE: The Venerable Bede (c.673–735) depicted using a quill pen. The quill pen had to be repeatedly dipped into the ink.

Pens that could be called "fountain pens"—carrying their own supply of ink—have been around for a very long time, although today the name tends to refer to pens with a specialized metal nib. Originally, pens used quill nibs, usually made from specially shaped bird feathers, usually swan.

The earliest recorded "fountain pens" are said to date from the 10th century, but it was in France, during the 17th and 18th centuries, that metal nibs were first introduced. These early pens were filled using an eyedropper. In the 19th and early 20th centuries designs for pens with a rubber reservoir built in to the body of the pen began to proliferate, as did methods for filling them with ink.

Some of the early designs were poor at controlling the amount of ink supplied to the nib, resulting in large blots of ink on the paper or the nib drying up. A New-York insurance broker, Lewis Waterman, solved this by inventing a system that allowed air into the rubber reservoir and controlled the amount of ink fed to the nib by narrow channels in the nib holder. He also developed an anti-corrosive metal tip for the nib. His patent was granted in 1884. The Parker pen, patented in 1905, used a button connected to a plate that compressed and released the tube to fill it with ink. The Sheaffer pen, patented in 1908, did the same job with a lever. The modern fountain pen had finally arrived.

THE INVENTION BY LADISLAV BIRO OF THE BALLPOINT PEN IN 1938, WHICH WAS QUICK AND CHEAP TO MAKE IN LARGE QUANTITIES AFTER WORLD WAR II, ENSURED THE DEMISE OF THE FOUNTAIN PEN.

THE SUPERMARKET

INVENTOR Michael Cullen **DATE** 1930 **COUNTRY** USA

In traditional grocery stores, the customer and shop assistant were separated by the counter and purchases were requested, usually meaning that only one customer at a time could be served.

The first self-service store is generally accepted to have opened in the 1920s in the USA and a chain of these known as the "Piggly-Wiggly" stores became widespread and popular. The obvious advantage to the retailer of this was that more goods could be sold in less time and with less labor cost, and that goods could be bought by customers in greater quantity, reducing the price paid. There was a cost in policing such stores against theft, but this was outweighed by the benefits.

The first genuine supermarket was probably opened in the USA; the credit usually goes to a Michael Cullen, whose "King Kullen" store opened in 1930 in New York. It led to the opening of a total of 17 stores in the chain. Very quickly, the supermarket store became widespread throughout the USA and Europe, enabling large numbers of people to shop more quickly and more cheaply.

ABOVE: A 1940s supermarket with shopping carts. The first shopping cart was invented in 1937 by Sylvan Goldman, owner of the Piggly-Wiggly supermarket chain. The cart had a metal frame, wheels and wire baskets. It was awarded a patent in 1940 and mass-production began.

THE HOVERCRAFT

INVENTOR Sir Christopher Cockerell   **DATE** 1952   **COUNTRY** UK

ABOVE: Sir Christopher Cockerell, the inventor of the hovercraft, inspects the twin propeller SRN6 MK 6 in 1973.

RIGHT: The SRN1 experimental hovercraft is tested on the Thames, London, UK. In 1959 the SRN1 was the first hovercraft to be commercially produced.

The principles behind the hovercraft, or air-cushion vehicle (ACV), were developed by several engineers in different countries from 1870 onward. Many engineers had grappled with the problem of reducing a boat's friction on water by using a cushion of air.

An English naval engineer, Sir John Isaac Thornycroft, filed a number of patents in 1877, but none was put into practical effect. Other engineers experimented with designs, including the Soviet engineer Vladimir Levkov, who developed air-cushion boats for the Soviet navy.

However, Sir Christopher Cockerell, who developed and patented his ideas for what he called a "hovercraft" in 1952, is generally regarded as the first person to convert the principles into commercially viable designs. The first practical passenger-carrying hovercraft, the SRN1, was launched in 1959. Larger, more practical craft were built to carry passengers and cars, and commercial Hoverspeed vehicles provided services across the English Channel until 2000, when competition from more efficient rival catamarans and Channel Tunnel trains rendered them obsolete. Smaller hovercraft are still used around the globe in specialist applications today, to travel across marshy terrain, and several large vehicles are also in military service.

An engine drives a fan or impeller, which forces air underneath the vehicle which is surrounded by a "skirt." The air is forced out from under the skirt, and this lifts the vehicle above the surface of the ground or water on which it is sitting. Another engine, or a second drive from the same engine, is used to power the craft forward.

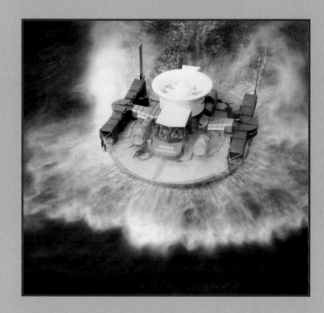

IN 1998, THE US POSTAL SERVICE BEGAN USING HOVERCRAFT TO TRANSPORT MAIL FROM BETHEL TO SEVEN REMOTE VILLAGES ALONG ALASKA'S KUSKOKWIM RIVER. THE SERVICE IS SUSPENDED FOR SEVERAL WEEKS EACH YEAR WHILE THE RIVER IS BEGINNING TO FREEZE.

THE TELEVISION

INVENTOR John Logie Baird   **DATE** 1926   **COUNTRY** UK

John Logie Baird is regarded as the inventor of television in the late 1920s in England, although many other people contributed to its development, both before and after Baird. In 1926 Baird successfully transmitted the first television picture with his mechanical system.

BELOW: Scottish-born John Logie Baird (1888–1946), the inventor of television, adjusting a transmitter.

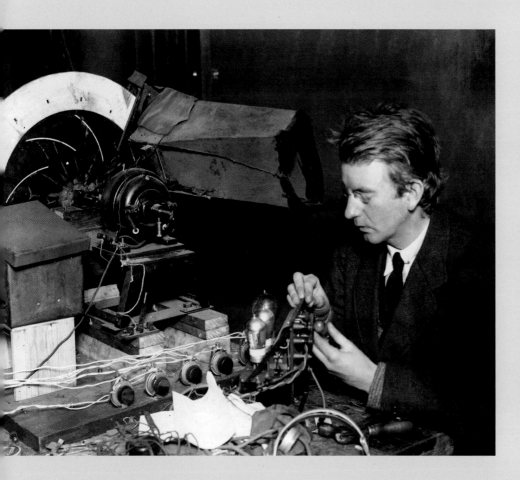

This used a camera consisting of a large spinning disc, with a spiral of holes. The early television sets were very basic and the picture often snowy. Most users could receive just one station—and only then if weather conditions were good.

The mechanical technology was replaced by electronic television in 1927, which Philo Farnsworth in San Francisco successfully demonstrated and then went on to patent. By 1936 there were about 200 television sets in use worldwide. Initially, television was available only in black and white, and even though experiments with color began in the 1920s, color televisions were not available until 1953.

More than any other invention, the television has influenced how people use their leisure time. But the television dominates more than our leisure time. From waging wars and fighting political campaigns to selling soap and ideas—all are vastly affected by Baird's invention.

ALTHOUGH ONLY 0.5 PERCENT OF HOUSEHOLDS IN THE USA HAD
A TELEVISION SET IN 1946, THAT FIGURE HAD JUMPED TO ALMOST
56 PERCENT IN 1954, AND TO 90 PERCENT BY 1962.

CHOCOLATE

DISCOVERERS Aztecs   **DATE** Ancient   **COUNTRY** Mexico

Like all great inventions and discoveries, can we imagine a world without chocolate? Although 4,000 years ago the ancient Egyptians enjoyed eating sweets, chocolate wasn't available until the ancient Aztec and Mayan cultures discovered the value of the cacao plant.

RIGHT: Hernanado Cortéz (1485–1547) meets with the Aztec emperor Montezuma in 1519. During his conquest of the Aztec empire, Cortéz was served a chocolate drink by Montezuma. Intrigued, Cortéz took some cacao beans back with him to Spain, where the originally bitter drink was sweetened with sugar and soon became popular.

They made a drink called "xocoatl" (meaning "warm liquid") from its beans. In 1519, during his conquest of Mexico, the Spanish explorer Hernán Cortés discovered chocolate at the court of the Aztec Emperor Montezuma, who reportedly drank it 50 or more times daily. However, it took until the mid-17th century for chocolate to find its way into Europe. Chocolate houses opened up and, because it was very expensive, the rich were soon happily consuming chocolate rolls and cakes.

Milk chocolate was invented in 1876 by Daniel Peter of Vevey, Switzerland. He took his invention to a Swiss firm—Nestlé—which is today the world's largest producer of chocolate. In 1879 Rodolphe Lindt of Berne, Switzerland, produced chocolate that melted on the tongue.

Today, the USA leads the world in cocoa bean importation and chocolate production, but Switzerland is the world leader for chocolate consumption per capita.

Chocolate contains phenylethylamine (PEA), a natural substance that is believed to stimulate the same reaction in the body as falling in love. For this reason it could be argued that a broken heart is an acceptable excuse for chocolate overindulgence.

"THE DIVINE DRINK ... WHICH BUILDS UP RESISTANCE AND FIGHTS FATIGUE."

A DESCRIPTION OF CHOCOLATE BY THE 16TH-CENTURY SPANISH EXPLORER HERNÁN CORTÉS

PICTURE CREDITS